The Decompress

CW00554350

Published by The Dive Informa

First edition 2003

British Library Cataloguing in Publication Data

Cole Bob

The Decompression Matrix

ISBN 0 9520934 2 1

Designed, typeset and produced by:
The Dive Information Company
25 Old Tye Avenue
Biggin Hill
Kent, TN16 3LY
ENGLAND

Tel / Fax: + 44 (0) 1959 572387

E-mail: bob.cole@diveinformation.co.uk

Printed by Sandford Press Ltd, Reading, ENGLAND

- Front cover *artwork by Ben Cole* -

"Which small bubble should I follow?"

Disclaimer

Important

Because people vary in their susceptibility to decompression illness, no decompression system can guarantee the total avoidance of decompression illness: even if the limitations of the system are complied with in full. Diving is a risk sport!

Special message

Because of the dangerous nature of diving, all participants take FULL responsibility for any accident and NO WARRANTY concerning advice in this book is expressed or implied. Under no circumstances will the author be liable or responsible for any consequential damages.

Caution

Do not implement any of the advice within this book without first obtaining appropriate training from a responsible diver training agency.

WARNING

You should be aware that the author is an engineer and not medically qualified, therefore has no right to make recommendations about decompression or recompression. If you buy this book, use its information and continue to dive, you can't say that you've not been warned!

Foreword

Decompression is a complex subject that is often poorly understood. Furthermore, personal decompression computers (PDCs) are an almost universal component of a recreational diver's kit. Yet many divers have no more than a cursory knowledge of how the PDC works, its many advantages and equally important, its limitations.

In this book, Bob Cole has taken a brave step in producing a specially useful explanation of decompression, predisposing factors and the workings of a range of PDCs. Having drawn on his immense experience and knowledge as an engineer and enthusiastic diver-user, he has written a reader-friendly and highly practical manual. Cole has proven that he is one of the few gifted people who not only fully understand a complex, jargon-riddled subject, but can also explain it in straightforward, waffle-free English.

I thoroughly recommend this book to any and every diver, regardless of the decompression system used.

Dr John Bevan
Managing Director
Submex (London)
Sub Sea Consultants

Preface

Diving is a risk sport, and because of this the only way to avoid decompression illness (DCI) is not to dive. But that's stupid! You might as well say go to work, and everyone knows that WORK is a four letter word invented for those who don't dive.

Why write another book on decompression? You'd think at my time of life that I would know better! Well, I've been lecturing on the subject for the SAA, Uwatec, Suunto and others for more than 30 years, and I like it. I don't like seeing my diving friends and others getting hurt, and I like the idea of sharing information. This book is a follow up to "Decompression and Computer Assisted Diving", published in 1993, and is based upon my decompression lectures developed since then. Having no formal notes, I simply talk to the slides, so this book is also for those people who ask for a copy of my notes. The graphics are also taken from those lectures.

In the real world of sport diving DCI avoidance is a multifaceted issue that requires an holistic approach. When knowledge of physiology, physics and risk are coupled together with an understanding of the limitations of personal decompression computers (PDCs), decompression tables and diving practice, the decompression matrix is solved and divers are better placed to protect themselves against DCI.

The 40 metre depth limit set by some diver training agencies is not a guarantee of safety. Safety is a relative thing. Some divers are dangerous in 10 metres of water. The key to safer diving is preparation. Fabio Amaral set up the Bikini Atoll Dive Centre, in the Central Pacific, and ran it for six years until November 2001. During that time he dived twice a day to 45 metres plus without incident, clocking up an impressive 1137 dives in the process. It is estimated that during that period customers and staff made over 20,000 decompression exposures diving twice a day to the nuclear wrecks, 40 metres plus, below in the lagoon. In all there was just one confirmed DCI case and two divers were reported as feeling unwell during the flight home. Accepting that the latter of the two, in unconfirmed reports, did in fact contract DCI, this is a 1 in 6,666 risk of DCI (or 0.015% bend rate). By example, Fabio has shown us the value of good thinking, good dive planning and good dive preparation. Furthermore, it is interesting to note that in the history of Bikini diving no Dive Master, Assistant Dive Master or Guide suffered any form of DCI. Perhaps this is a case for some useful scientific research

When applied thoughtfully, knowledge is non-destructive, non-polluting and may provide self-protection for the diver. Risk can be reduced and safety improved.

Bob Cole

Contents

My thanks to:

My wife Lesley for her love and for her efforts with the proof reading.

My sons Matthew and Benjamin for the constant help they give to this computer illiterate fool.

Professor Alan Bird for the use of his retinal fluorescein angiography photographs.

Dr John Bevan, Submex Ltd, London.

Dr John King, London Hyperbaric Services Harley Street London, for his friendship and medical advice.

Mark Cooper for his help and support, which he owes me anyway because I taught him the "Brownie-point System", and his valued friendship.

Dr Nick McIver, Fakenham Norfolk UK for his help in obtaining a photograph of an "amplatzer".

Dr Ian M Calder, TD MD DSc MRCP FRCPath FHKCPath FFOM DMJ(Path).

Tony Marshall Managing Director of Collins and Chambers, London E8 for our long standing friendship, for his help and advice over too many years to recall.

John Sinclair of Suunto Diving UK for his constant belief in me and his ready willingness to help.

Bill Clayton of Sandford Press for his friendship, help and advice with all printing matters.

Dr John Harrison MB ChB FRCA, Medical Director of hyperbaric unit, NWWERU, Wirral, UK.

Dr Phil Bryson, Medical Director of The Diving Diseases Research Centre, Devon, England.

Peter Marquis, Remote Heath Care Manager, Plymouth Hospital, NHS Trust.

Martin Hoddlestone for his views on what aspiring Technical divers need from a book like this.

Bret Gillam, President of Scuba Diving International (SDI) and Technical Diving International (TDI).

Fabio Amaral, Former Dive Master of Bikini Atoll for his encouragement and friendship.

Mike Dudas, Assistant Dive Master Bikini Atoll for his useful comments on the first draft.

Chris Hellas for his friendship and advice.

Paperlink 356, Kennington Road, London SE11 4LD for Fig 6.21.

Mike Barry for his professional proof reading.

References

Hawkins JA, Shilling CW & Hansen RA (1935) a suggested change in calculating decompression tables for diving. Nav. Med, Wash. 33, 327-338.

Yarbrough OD: 1937 Calculation of Decompression Tables. Research report, USN Experimental Diving Unit, Washington DC.

Van Der Aue OE, Keller RJ, Brinton ES: The effect of exercise during decompression from increased barometric pressure on the incidence of decompression sickness in man. US Navy Experimental Diving Unit Report 8-49, 1949.

Ellsberg E (1929) On the Bottom. New York: Dodd, Mead.

Henry FM. The role of exercise in altitude pain. Am J Physiol 145:279-284, 1945.

Van Der Aue OE, Brinton ES and Kellar RJ (1945) Surface Decompression: Derivation and Testing of Decompression Tables with Safety Limits for Certain Depth and Exposures. NEDU Report 5-45. Panama City, Fla.: US Navy Experimental Diving Unit

Van Der Aue OE, Lellar RJ and Brinton ES (1949) The Effects of Exercise During Decompression from Increased Barometric Pressure on the Incidence of Decompression Sickness in Man. NEDU Report 8-49. Panama City, Fla.: US Navy Experimental Diving Unit.

Bühlmann AA (1975) Decompression theory: Swiss practice. In The Physiology and Medicine of Diving and Compressed Air work, 2nd Ed pp 348-365. Ed PB Bennett and DH Elliott. London: Bailière Tindall.

Vann RD (1989b) Exercise and circulation in the formation and growth of bubbles. In Supersaturation and Bubble Formation in Fluids and Organisms, pp 235-258. Ed A Brubakk, BB Hemmingsen and G Sundnes. Trondheim: Royal Norwegian Society of Sciences and Letters.

Masurel G, Guillerm R and Cavenal P (1976) Detection ultrasonore par effet Doppler de bulles circulates chez l'homme lors de 98 plongèes a l'air. Revue de Medecine Subaquatique et Hyperbare 15 (59), 199-201.

Nishi RY, Eatock BC, Buckingham IP and Ridgewell BA (1982) Assessment of Decompression Profiles by Ultrasonic Monitoring. Phase III: No-decompression Diving. DCIEM Report 82-R-38.

Evans A and Walder DN (19690 Significance of gas micro-nuclei in the aetiology of decompression sickness. Nature, London. 222. 251-252.

Vann RD (1982b) MK XV UBA Decompression Trials at Duke: A summary Report, Final Report on Office of Naval Research Contract N00014-77-0460.

Workman RD, 1965. Calculation of Decompression Schedules for Nitrogen-Oxygen and Helium-Oxygen Dives. Research Report 6-65, USN Experimental Diving Unit, Washington DC.

Eawcett EF and Blachford JV 1901. The Frequency of an Opening Between the Right and Left Auricles at the Septum of the Foetal Foramen Ovale. Jnl Antomy and Physiology; Vol 35 New series Vo 1 pages 67-70.

Van Der Aue OE, Keller RJ, Brinton ES, et al: Calculation and testing of decompression tables air dives employing the procedure of surface decompression and the use of oxygen. US Navy Experimental Diving Unit Report 13-51, 1951

Walder DN: Adaption to decompression sickness in caisson work. In Proceedings of the 3rd International Biometerology Congress. Oxford. 1968, pp 350-359.

Vann RD: 1982. Decompression theory and application. In Bennett, Elliott DH (eds): The Physiology and Medicine of Diving and Compressed Air Work. 2nd ed. London, Bailiere Tindall, 1975, pp 352-382.

Bühlmann AA: Decompression theory: Swiss practice. In Bennett, Elliott DH (eds): The Physiology and Medicine of Diving and Compressed Air Work. 2nd ed. London, Bailiere Tindall, 1975, pp348-365.

Lang MA and Lehner (eds). 2000. Proceedings of the Reverse Dive Profile workshop. October 29-30 1999. Smithsonian Institution, Washington DC. 295p.

Walder DN: 1973. Man in the deep. Part 1. Oceans 2000. 3rd World Congress of Underwater Activities. BSAC/CMAS, 1973, PP24-25.

Curley MD, Robin GJ and Thalmann ED (1989). Percentage body fat and human decompression. Underwater Biomed. Res. 16 (suppl.) abstract 33.

Wise DA (1963) Contitutional Facors in Decompression Sickness. NEDU Report 2-63. Panama City, Fla.: US Navy Experimental Diving Unit.

Haldane JS (1922) Respiration. New Haven, CT: Yale University Press.

Momsen CB (1942) Report on the Use of Helium-Oxygen Mixtures for Diving. NEDU Report 2-42, AD728758. Panama City, Fla.: US Navy Experimental Diving Unit.

Hills BA (1966) A Thermodynamic and Kinetic Approach to Decompression Sickness. PhD Thesis. University of Adelaide: Libraries Board of South Australia.

Hills BA and LeMessurier (1969) Unsaturation in living tissue relative to the pressure and composition of inhaled gas and its significance in decompression theory. Clin. Sci. 36, 185-195.

Darwin E (1774) Experiments on animals fluids in the exhausted receiver. Phil. Trans. 64, 344-349.

Harvey EN, Barnes DK, McElroy WD, Whiteley AH, Pease DC and Cooper KW (1944a) Bubble formation in animals. I. Physical factors. J Cells. Comp. Physiol. 24(1), 1-22.

Ikels KG (1970) Production of gas bubbles in fluids by tribonucleation. J. Appl. Physiol. 28, 524-527.

Eckenhoff RG (1992) Decompression-induced bubble formation in humans after shallow water dives. In proc. Repetitive Diving Workshop, pp 219-226. Ed MA Lang and RD Vann. AAUS Diving Safety Publication AAUSDSP-RDW-02-92. Costa Mesa, Calf: American Academy of Underwater Sciences.

Oxygen and the Diver, 1992. Prof. Kenneth Donald. The SPA Ltd Worcs UK ISBN 1 85421 176 5.

Kramer HJ AND Lichardus B (1986) Atrial natriuretic hormones - thirty years after the discovery of atrial volume receptors. Klin. Wschr. 64, 719-731.

Polkinghorne PK, Sehmi K, Cross MR, Minassian D and Bird AC (1988) Ocular fundus lesions in divers. Lancet ii, 1381 - 1383.

Divers Alert Network (1989) Report on 1988 Diving Accidents. DAN Carolina.

St Leger Dowse M, Bryson P, Gunby A and Fife W (1994) Men and Women in Diving. Diving Diseases Research Centre, England - ISBN 0 9525152 0 2.

Thomson L (2001) Doppler bubble monitoring of divers at Rothera Research Station, Antarctica, Phase 1: January - October 1999. Phase 2: December 2000 - February 2001 - For the British Antarctic Survey.

BHA Annual Conference, hosted by DDRC, 28th-30th September 2001 Exeter UK. Physiological factors predisposing to Decompression illness - a review. Dr Peter Wilmshurst Consultant Cardiologist, Shrewsbury.

Decompression and Computer Assisted Diving, 1993. Bob Cole. Diving Information Co, ISBN 0 9520934 0 5

SAA Bühlmann Decompression Handbook, 7th edition 1999. Bob Cole. Sub-Aqua Association (UK), ISBN 0 9519337 0 1

Rebreather Diving, 1998. Bob Cole. Sub-Aqua Association (UK), ISBN 0 9519337 9 5

SAA Nitrox Diving Student Notebook 2nd edition 1997, Bob Cole. Sub-Aqua Association (UK), ISBN 0 9519337 7 9

Chapter 1
In the beginning

A brief history of man underwater

Popular belief has it that diving started about 1943 with Cousteau and Gagnan's invention of the Aqualung. Although this was a major step forward and one that can't be over-estimated, diving started very much earlier.

Before equipment based diving came about, breath-hold diving was practised. In fact, archaeologists claim that Neanderthal man dived for food, and as far back as 4500 BC people were diving for shells and pearls as well as for food.

From the ancient Greeks to modern times fishermen have dived for sponges. Breath-holding or apnoea sponge diving continued until the nineteenth century when helmet diving gear was introduced. It is interesting to note that the Ancient Greeks were the first to set down the legal rights of divers and the goods they salvaged.

Diving is not and has never been a totally male dominated activity. The Ama, or diving women of Japan and Korea, see Fig 1.1, dived for pearls while the men acted as tenders.

For centuries divers have been involved in military operations. In the Trojan Wars (1194-1184 BC) they were used to sabotage enemy ships by cutting anchor ropes or drilling holes in hulls etc. Divers have also played a more constructive role in assisting in the building of bridges and the salvaging of wrecks. In fact, history is littered with the deeds of divers.

Early equipment

Equipment used by modern recreational divers has evolved over hundreds of years; however, the greatest advances have been made in the last 50 years. Nevertheless, it is instructive to take a look back in time at some of the important waypoints.

The simplest yet most important device used by all divers is the snorkel, or breathing tube. This simple tube allows the diver to breathe while lying on the surface of the water, face down, watching fish. If your diet is fish and you don't have a supermarket on your island this is very useful in helping you to survive. Breathing tubes were, and still are in some places, made of reed or bamboo. Modern examples are

Fig 1.2

made of plastic and can be fitted with an array of self-draining devices, flexible mouthpieces and valves to stop them flooding whilst underwater. There is a physical limit on the length of a snorkel tube, however many people have tried to design a long snorkel to allow the diver to descend and still breathe. In 1511 one such design by Vegetius blocked the diver's vision and created such a tremendous burden on the diver's chest that it was impossible to breathe. The maximum length of a snorkel is about 450mm (18 inches), beyond this breathing becomes difficult.

Assyrian Frieze drawings dated about 900 BC, see Fig 1.2, depict the use of a diving bell. Diving Bells are rigid structures filled with air from which divers could work whilst underwater. One important device was designed and patented in 1691 by the English astronomer Edmond Halley. Halley's bell was supplied with air from weighted

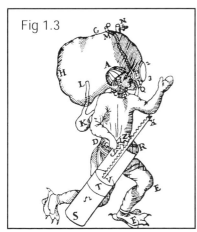

Fig 1.3

barrels, which were hauled from the surface. Dives of up to ninety minutes were recorded at depths of 20 metres.

Even Leonardo da Vinci took an interest in diving. His drawings show diving sets and fins. In the light of current knowledge it can be seen that the snorkel tube has a very large so-called "dead space". This would allow carbon dioxide to build-up in the tube, which would cause distress to the diver. In another of his designs he used a "wine skin" to contain breathing air.

This was probably the first rebreather. Again, there was a major error in design. The "wine skin" breathing bag would not only hold fresh air but also retain the diver's exhaled breath. Later in 1680, Giovanni Borelli recognised da Vinci's mistake and that the air would need purification before it could be breathed again. It might be said that with this idea he had invented a basic rebreather, see Fig 1.3.

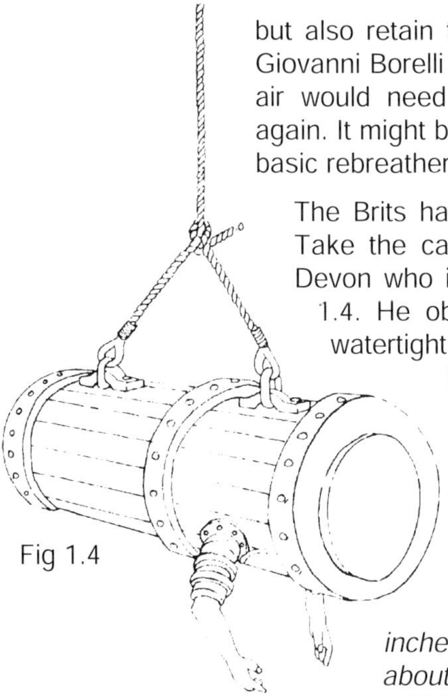

The Brits have always been in the forefront of diving. Take the case of John Lethbridge of Newton Abbot, Devon who in 1715 invented a diving engine, see Fig 1.4. He observed that a diving machine should be watertight and able to withstand pressure without being cumbersome. The cidermakers of Devon provided the concept of a barrel. So he turned to a cooper in Stanhope Street, London to construct what Lethbridge described as: *"It is made of wainscot perfectly round, about six feet in length, about two and a half feet in diameter at the head, and about eighteen inches in diameter at the foot, and it contains about thirty gallons; it is hooped with iron hoops within and without to guard against pressure. ...."*

Fig 1.4

Lethbridge died on the 11th of December 1759 after a very successful salvage diving career around the World. A note was made in the Wolborough parish church register. *"Buried Mr Lethbridge, inventor of a most famous diving engine, by which he recovered from the bottom of the sea, in different parts of the globe, almost £100,000 for the English and Dutch merchants which had been lost by shipwreck".*

Fig 1.5

In the nineteenth century and during the industrial revolution divers were used on civil engineering projects eg bridges, salvage, mining etc.

In England, 1829, John and Charles Deane produced the Standard Diving Dress. This consisted of a rigid helmet and flexible waterproof suit weighted down with weights and heavy lead boots, see Fig 1.5. Air was pumped from the surface, by hand, down to the diver's helmet. In later suits the diver could adjust his

Fig 1.6

buoyancy by controlling the volume of air in the suit. Many other companies around the world have followed this basic design adding their own modifications. This type of equipment, with refinements, can still be found in use today.

Rebreathers

In 1878 an Englishman called Henry Fleuss devised an oxygen rebreather set which cleaned the re-circulating gas of carbon dioxide by passing it over rope soaked in caustic potash, see Fig 1.6. Khotinsky & Lake discovered the first true carbon dioxide absorbent, Barium Hydroxide, in 1881. Work on rebreathers was also going on in Germany, and it was Drägerwerk who in 1907, demonstrated an underwater sled. This sled was equipped with a rebreather that had an underwater duration of two hours.

These sets used pure oxygen and while this gas has a depth limit of about eight metres, it produces no decompression problems.

Clammy death

During the first World War, Italy developed a human torpedo which was used to attack and sink an Austrian battleship in Pola Harbour. They were at it again during the Second World War and attacked Allied shipping in Gibraltar. The Italian frogmen used a two man human torpedo nicknamed "Maiale" or "pig". The British responded with their own two man torpedo called a "Chariot" and the divers were called "Charioteers". The Sladen dry suits worn by Charioteers were nicknamed "Clammy Death" because of the damp cold feeling they caused.

Decompression illness (the bends)

 In the field of tunnelling and Standard Dress air diving, problems were being experienced with the divers' "bends". From his 1878 experiments in Paris, Paul Bert concluded that the bends culprit was excess nitrogen in the blood that caused bubbles to form. The leading scientists of the time thought that the illness was caused by the difference in pressure between the nitrogen inside the diver's body and that outside.

To combat this problem it was thought that the pressure on the diver or tunnel worker should be reduced slowly. This would allow the excess nitrogen in the body to escape harmlessly. In 1900, Heller, Mager and Von-Schötter of Vienna suggested that the rate of ascent for a diver should be 20 minutes for every 10 metres of water or for the tunnel worker 20 minutes for each atmosphere of pressure. Following this procedure guaranteed one of two outcomes: either the diver was well when he surfaced or he was not! A diver who became ill was dumped back into the water, taken to depth and then brought back to the surface even more slowly. He either got better - or he didn't. If he didn't he hobbled home to get on with the rest of his life, whatever that meant! The unlucky ones died from this haphazard treatment. In the latter two cases the man was usually considered unsuitable for diving. In any event there was a lot of human debris from this activity.

Fig 1.7

Professor J S Haldane
From the Nick Baker collection

In the early part of the twentieth century it became clear to the Royal Navy that it was time for a more considered approach to diving and decompression. So, the Sea Lords appointed John Scott Haldane, see Fig 1.7, to investigate and report back. The Navy's brief to Haldane was ..."to devise a method whereby the average man of sufficient aptitude can do useful work at a depth of 180 feet (55 metres)". The really clever part of the brief was the part that said ..."the average man of sufficient aptitude"... , clearly the Navy was not looking for Superman or his brother.

Haldane and his team Dr A E Boycott and Lieutenant G C C Damant RN researched the problem and produced a scientific paper in 1908 entitled "The prevention of compressed air illness". The system recognised that nitrogen was distributed around the body by the blood and that different body tissues accepted and eliminated nitrogen at differing rates. For the purposes of the diving being undertaken, Haldane assigned five mathematical tissue compartments to describe the ebb and flow of nitrogen and when the diver must return to the surface. The rate of ascent chosen, 60 foot per minute caused alarm. However, it proved safe for the type of diving at the time and the system was accepted and adopted by the Royal Navy.

Many other navies around the world also used this system. However, it proved on certain dives to have shortcomings and has been modified by the different users to meet their own requirements. Essentially, the system is the base of all current systems and has stood the test of time.

Gases other than air

Fig 1.8

The Italian frogmen used oxygen rebreathers, which had a depth limitation of about eight metres. The British Charioteers were equipped with Nitrox rebreathers to overcome this severe depth limitation, see Fig 1.8.

Breathing air under pressure causes a number of problems, notably nitrogen narcosis. This is an effect much like alcohol intoxication except that it is brought on by pressure. The effects start at about 30 metres where the diver may start to feel rather jolly. As depth increases mood changes and divers become less able to concentrate. This can, at depths in excess of 50 metres, become a severe limitation. It was found that substituting helium for the nitrogen overcame the problem. Between the two World Wars the Americans did a great deal of research on this topic.

Research into decompression, the effects of different gas mixes, and other diver related issues is still going on. The gains made are slow and hard-earned.

For deep diving the professional diver will use saturation techniques. In this system, a bell or habitat is lowered to the working depth zone with the divers. During the operation they live in the bell at the ambient pressure, donning their diving gear to go to work. The system avoids the need to

Fig 1.9

return to the surface after each dive, thus saving time and money wasted during non-productive lengthy decompression schedules. For the divers this is a safer method because it avoids multiple decompressions where they are exposed to the possibility of the bends (decompression illness). Recreational or sport divers do not use this technique.

Modern recreational diving

Although Cousteau and Gagnan's aqualung is the basis of the vast majority of all recreational diving equipment, it is difficult to say that they are the fathers of British diving. In the 50s when diving started to take-off, it was the BBC television's wildlife programmes by Hans and Lotte Hass, see Fig 1.9, that fired the imaginations of would be divers. Every other Sunday, wannabe divers were glued to their black and white TV sets waiting for Lotte to swim to the seabed. In the late 50s Lloyd Bridges who played Mike Nelson, see Fig 1.10, in the fictional series Sea Hunt reinforced this. Recreational diving was on its way!

Fig 1.10

A true story about the power of Sea Hunt: One Sunday afternoon, during the winter of 1960, I called on my friend and diving buddy Pete Gosling. His mother answered the door "Hello Mrs Gosling, is Peter in?" I asked. "Yes" she said shaking her head and tutting. "What's wrong?" I said . . . "You'll find out, he's in the front room." I pushed open the front room door to see Peter sitting on the edge of the sofa with his fins, mask and snorkel-tube on and watching Sea Hunt on the television. "What the hell are you doing?" He took the snorkel from his mouth, looked at me and said "You've got to get into the spirit of things." Putting the snorkel back he returned to the TV and his dream world. Gosling was 29 at the time, he never really grew up. Nor did I, the child is still alive! Thank goodness!

Modern diving gear

Diving cylinders have come a long way since those early days when they had a maximum working pressure of 120 atmospheres (bar) and free air capacity of between 700 litres and 1120 litres (25 and 40 cubic feet for you oldies). Popular sized modern cylinders have working pressures of around 232 bar with free air capacities of between 2320 and 3480: an improvement of over 300%. Breathing valves, the so-called "demand valve regulators" (DVs), have also greatly improved; with the first and second stages being separated with down-stream balanced valves providing previously unheard of volumes of breathing gas for minimum breathing effort. By comparison divers needed to suck air from the early valves. Decompression tables that have their origins in Haldanean methods are being replaced by wrist-mounted personal decompression computers (PDCs) that calculate the diver's decompression obligation in real-time. Some PDCs systems measure breathing rates from the first stage of the DV and use a radio transmitter to relay the information to the wrist decompression computer.

Chapter 2
Traditional decompression

Introduction

Diving should be impossible!

Without a doubt diving should be impossible. However, through the invention of the diving helmet and Rebreather in the 19th century and the Open Circuit Aqua Lung in the 20th century, people dive regularly. The success of these efforts is, for the most part, good. Nevertheless, each year there are a number of deaths and decompression accidents. This book is concerned, in the main, with providing divers with information that will help them to avoid decompression illness (DCI), which may also reduce the number of deaths, by a small amount.

An inappropriate release of energy.

The breathing gas used by divers is compressed into diving cylinders and when released by the demand valve regulator (DV), some of the stored energy is liberated. If the pressure is released too quickly the DV will become very cold and may freeze up . . . this is an inappropriate release of energy. Similarly, decompression illness (DCI) comes about by an inappropriate exchange of energy: the stored energy in the dissolved gas is released to form free-gas (bubbles) ie by ascending too fast, failing to make correct decompression stops, and/or unsuitable surface intervals.

Everyone decompresses.

What is decompression? The answer is very simple: decompression is any reduction in ambient pressure. Everyone, divers and non-divers alike, decompresses at some time or other. Take changing weather conditions, for example. On day one Britain may be covered by a high pressure weather zone. If that zone moves to mainland Europe on day two and is replaced by a low pressure zone, then the whole population of Britain will experience decompression because of the reduction in pressure, see Fig 1.1. Decompression can happen in other situations, such as when ascending hills and

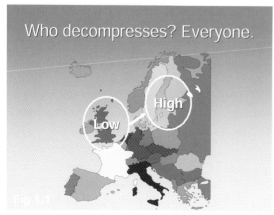

Who decompresses? Everyone.

mountains or flying in an aircraft. Decompression occurs in both open cockpit planes and commercial airliners. Commercial airliners limit the pressure drop for their passengers by pressurising the aircraft cabin. However, decompression still occurs for pilots and passengers because aeroplanes are only pressurised to about 2400m and not to sea level.

These forms of decompression do not cause decompression illness (DCI) - the so-called "bends". This is because over the years humans have evolved the capacity to adapt to slow, minor changes in pressure. These pressure changes are small, in the order of millibars, and take place over a relatively long time. Decompression is said to be appropriate when the body can cope adequately. The human body is adaptable to pressure changes and provided one stays within nature's limits, this can be used when diving.

All divers do it (decompress that is) and, all dives involve decompression. Decompression occurs when a diver rises to a lesser depth, no matter how small that rise might be. As the diver enters the underwater world, pressure increases at a high rate with increased depth - bars rather than millibars.

Time too becomes a most important factor in calculations. Therefore the diver must be aware of the importance of the speed of these high pressure changes. During a dive, compressed air (most of it nitrogen) is dissolved into the body. This is because nature is trying to equalise the gas tension within the body with the increase in gas pressure in the lungs.

When the diver ascends to a lesser depth, the ambient pressure of the water reduces. The body compensates for this reduction by trying to expel the accumulated excess dissolved nitrogen to equalise the pressure difference. If the rate of elimination is within the limits set by evolution, then decompression is said to be appropriate and the dive will be a safe one.

Decompression illness (DCI) occurs where pressure changes on ascent exceed nature's limits. Some of the excess nitrogen dissolved in the body is released from solution to form bubbles (free-gas) in the blood and/or body

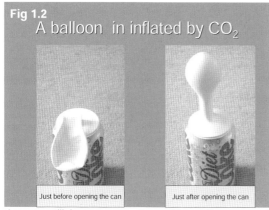

Fig 1.2
A balloon in inflated by CO_2

Just before opening the can | Just after opening the can

Are you still in any doubt?

Bubbles choke or occlude the system.

tissues. This "bubble trouble" causes a range of adverse outcomes and effects. It is the size and location of these, mainly nitrogen, bubbles that determine the severity of the illness.

If you are in any doubt about the power of this energy release, try opening a can of coca cola quickly. The pressure in such a can is about 3.2bar, this is equal to the pressure of nitrogen created on a dive of just 30 metres, Fig 1.2!

Bubbles so released may cause a disturbance in blood flow choking (occluding) the oxygen supply to tissues down stream of the insult, see Fig 1.3, and/or may cause deformation of tissue, and/or cause the deformation of nerves.

A variety of signs and symptoms can be produced from itching skin or joint pain through to major damage to the brain and/or spinal cord, ie the central nervous system (CNS). There are many variations in between these extremes. Some forms of decompression illness can also kill.

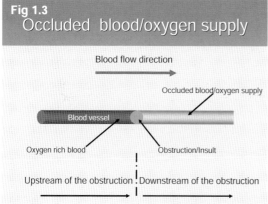

Fig 1.3
Occluded blood/oxygen supply

Blood flow direction

Occluded blood/oxygen supply

Blood vessel

Oxygen rich blood | Obstruction/Insult

Upstream of the obstruction | Downstream of the obstruction

On the other hand, the bubbles may be very small (micro or silent bubbles): these restrict the elimination of excess nitrogen for a limited period until they themselves diffuse out causing no other detectable signs or symptoms.

For over 100 years, scientists throughout the world have been working hard to find ways of making it safe to work underwater. Although very little research has been done directly for amateur divers, we have benefited from naval and commercial work. Rules have been formulated which give a degree of protection to the diver provided these rules are closely followed.

Today, these rules come in the form of decompression tables and, latterly, personal decompression computers (PDCs). It is important to understand that neither is infallible. Both are merely based upon mathematical models of the human body in terms of the uptake and elimination of excess nitrogen. It is also very important to remember that all tables and most PDCs are fixed in their mode of operation and take no account of diver behaviour factors. However, there are some PDCs available that adjust their basic design parameters according to actual diving behaviour and the underwater environment. These PDCs are more sensitive to the diver's decompression needs. Nevertheless, even these PDCs are not infallible

PDCs do not account for real nitrogen movement. Only the theoretical changes.

Furthermore, tables and PDCs assume that divers are fit and well. It is up to divers to ensure that they are medically and mentally fit to dive and that other factors which might influence the performance of the tables or PDC have been avoided or taken into account. Has the diver had a cold within the last ten days? Has the diver been drinking or suffering from a hangover? Is the diver intending to work underwater? Is the water cold? All these factors must be taken into consideration before the dive. These are jobs that Tables and PDCs can't do. This is where the diver must turn the brain on and think!

Are you fit and well?

Have you been drinking?

This is a major area of diver education. Furthermore, diver education is not a one off exercise - get an open water certificate and forget it! For long term well-being, diver education is a lifelong process of continuous personal development.

PDCs can't do all the work.

Life long learning will help protect you.

This book sets out to fill in some of the holes left, due to limited space and the desire not to confuse or frighten trainees, in basic training manuals. Hopefully, it provides a wider understanding of the issues involved and improves the chance of DCI free diving.

More than basic training.

Traditional decompression theory

Current decompression practice is based upon the work of Haldane, Boycott and Damant. The following text explores Haldane's four principles.

In his 1908 paper "The Prevention of Compressed Air Illness" Haldane introduced four main principles relating to decompression that are of great significance.

Haldane's four main principles of decompression are:

1 The uptake and elimination of gas by a tissue takes the exponential form.

2 The rate of saturation varies from tissue to tissue.

3 The gas *tension in a tissue should never exceed approximately twice the ambient pressure.

4 Decompression should be initiated by a relatively large drop in ambient pressure.

1. The uptake and elimination of gas by a tissue takes the exponential form.

What does this mean? At the surface under normal conditions, the diver is said to be at equilibrium with the atmosphere. The body makes use of the oxygen in the air. Although there is a small difference (the so-called "oxygen window"), between the gas tension on the arterial side of the circulatory system compared with the gas tension in the tissues and venous side, no net exchange of nitrogen occurs. This will be discussed later, see Chapter 3.

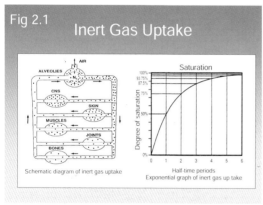

Fig 2.1
Inert Gas Uptake

Schematic diagram of inert gas uptake

Exponential graph of inert gas up take

As the diver descends, the ambient pressure on the body increases, causing the breathing air (mainly nitrogen) to dissolve into the body tissues (Henry's Law) via the lungs and bloodstream, see Fig 2.1. This occurs at a rate proportional to the mix of gases that the diver is breathing (Dalton's Law). During and following ascent, the reverse is true and gas is released from the tissues, see Fig 2.2. Oxygen is metabolised by the body and is not considered to contribute to decompression illness. This is not the case with nitrogen.

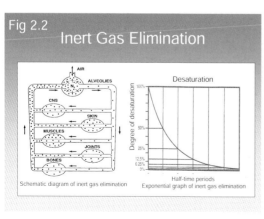

Fig 2.2
Inert Gas Elimination

Schematic diagram of inert gas elimination

Exponential graph of inert gas elimination

Changes in body tissue tension are not instantaneous. There is a delay and the rate at which the changes take place varies with time: relatively quickly at the beginning but slowing down as time goes on. The way in which nitrogen is absorbed and eliminated by the body is described by the exponential form (ie the shape of the graph in Figs 2.1 and 2.2) In other words, there is a fixed relationship between time and the movement of gas in or out of the body in response to an external pressure change, provided that there are no micro-bubbles.

This concept might be easier to understand by using the example of water pouring from a hole of a certain diameter in the bottom of a water-butt to represent the flow of nitrogen from the body. If a full butt of water takes, say, five minutes to drain to the half-full level, it will then take another five minutes to drain half the balance. Simply expressed: the remaining balances are drained by half every five minutes. This five minute span is called a half-time period or just half-time, see Fig 2.3. In theory, at this rate, the water-butt will never completely drain. In practice, however, after six half-time periods (in this case a total of thirty minutes) the water-butt is considered, by convention, to be empty. The same is true for the uptake and elimination of nitrogen in the body.

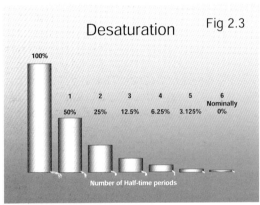

Fig 2.3
Desaturation

100%

1 — 50%
2 — 25%
3 — 12.5%
4 — 6.25%
5 — 3.125%
6 Nominally 0%

Number of Half-time periods

Now take an identical water-butt, this time with a hole half the area of the one mentioned above. In this case, the half-time is doubled to ten minutes. The process is the same except that in this instance it will take sixty minutes to drain the water-butt. If the hole were halved again, then the half-time would be doubled to twenty minutes and so on. The concept of reducing hole size in the water-butt creating longer half-times is analogous to the reduction in the size of blood vessels as they progress further from the heart. This is the way nitrogen is taken up and eliminated by the body. It is accepted as a legitimate process by most modern table designers.

In his Tables, Bühlmann adapted this process further by including a factor in his calculations to account for the water vapour produced as air is moistened in the nose and mouth spaces and air passages. At 98.4ºF/37ºC body temperature, the lungs constantly contain 0.063 Atm/bar water vapour pressure which is independent of ambient pressure. Free-gas (micro or silent bubbles) caused during ascents and decompression also inhibit the elimination of excess nitrogen and Bühlmann and others take this factor into account in the formulation of their tables.

2. The rate of saturation varies from tissue to tissue

Gas enters the body via the lungs and diffuses through the thin wall of the alveoli into the bloodstream, from where it is transported around the circulatory system to the various body tissues. The nitrogen uptake is governed by a number of factors: the difference in nitrogen tension across the lung/blood interface and across the blood/tissue interface; the rate of blood flow (perfusion); the number of capillaries supplying the tissue, and the tissue's receptivity to the dissolved gases.

Haldane determined that the different body tissues take up and eliminate gas at different rates. Tissues with high perfusion rates, served by a large network of blood vessels - such as the brain - became known as fast tissues because of their ability to move gas in and out quickly.

Other tissues with a smaller blood supply - such as fatty tissue - take up and eliminate gas at a slower rate, despite having a larger capacity for nitrogen. These were called slow tissues. For more information, see Chapter 3.

Remember the analogy of the hole in the water-butt: the different hole sizes in the bottom of the butt represent the different sizes of arteries and veins in the body. A large hole, with a high flow rate, represents fast tissue, while smaller holes illustrate the action of slower tissues.

Haldane constructed a mathematical model on the basis of five tissues; each is a theoretical compartment and not an actual body tissue. Each tissue compartment was assigned

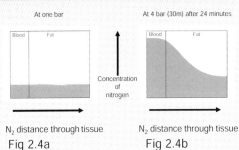

Distribution of Nitrogen through a Unit of Tissue

At one bar

| Blood | Fat |

N₂ distance through tissue

Fig 2.4a

At 4 bar (30m) after 24 minutes

| Blood | Fat |

Concentration of nitrogen

N₂ distance through tissue

Fig 2.4b

The values shown here are absolute pressure (bar).

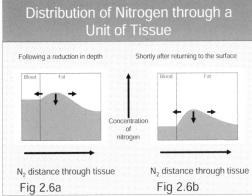

Distribution of Nitrogen through a Unit of Tissue

At 4 bar (30m) after 4.5hrs

| Blood | Fat |

N₂ distance through tissue

Fig 2.5a

At 4 bar (30m) after 8hrs

| Blood | Fat |

Concentration of nitrogen

N₂ distance through tissue

Fig 2.5b

Distribution of Nitrogen through a Unit of Tissue

Following a reduction in depth

| Blood | Fat |

N₂ distance through tissue

Fig 2.6a

Shortly after returning to the surface

| Blood | Fat |

Concentration of nitrogen

N₂ distance through tissue

Fig 2.6b

a half-time period of 5, 10, 20, 40 and 75 minutes respectively. It was accepted at the time that the human body is far more complex than this broad brush approach, but the model was thought adequate for the decompression needs of the time. It seems that the rate of gas exchange in a given tissue can vary depending upon perfusion. Blood flow, to say muscle, varies during a dive depending upon work rate and in any event is usually slower during the ascent and stops.

In the case of fatty tissue fed with blood from one side, gas exchange will be more nearer the blood vessels than away from them. Nitrogen will first be diffused into the cells adjacent to the blood vessels and then from these cells into neighbouring cells further from the blood supply.

Time is a most important factor in the distribution of nitrogen within the body and affects the type of decompression illness presented. Furthermore, it seems possible for nitrogen to diffuse further into fatty tissue, even when the ambient pressure is reduced. Fig 2.4a shows, at sea-level, a schematic unit area of tissue at equilibrium (ie pressure between the blood/tissue interface is balanced). If this section of tissue is now subjected to an absolute pressure of four Atm/bar (ie 100ft/30m) the tissue would try to gain equilibrium, see Figs 2.4b to 2.5b.

The blood will saturate quite quickly, but the fat will take much longer. In the region of eight hours. However, it isn't that simple. As the diver ascends and the ambient pressure drops, the nitrogen in the fatty tissue redistributes across the whole tissue instead of just flowing back towards the blood vessels to escape from the body, see Fig 2.6a. This is in response to lower saturation levels in neighbouring cells.

In fact, as the diver rises to a lesser depth, some fatty tissues near the blood supply may still be taking in nitrogen, see Fig 2.6b, which shows the situation shortly after surfacing. As the pressure decreases, nitrogen is drawn out of the cells next to the blood vessel into the blood. At the same time, nitrogen from the higher loaded cells diffuses into cells with a lower loading. In this instance it could be said that the fatty tissue, as a whole, is behaving as if it were a range of tissue - from fast to slow - combined in a single unit.

This concept suggests that this tissue compartment represents a micro rather than macro tissue region. Probably for this reason the US Navy extended its spectrum of tissues, from Haldane's original five to six tissue compartments, PADI moved to eight and Bühlmann used 16; with half-times ranging from four to 635 minutes, see Fig 2.7.

With this modification, Bühlmann's table model deals with the problems related to repetitive diving and flying after diving where the rate of elimination is crucial for planning subsequent dives. The number of theoretical tissue compartments personal decompression computers (PDCs) use, ranges from six to about nine depending upon the manufacturer and model.

Flying after diving is analogous to surfacing following another dive; the ambient pressure is reduced still further which causes the body's tissue compartments to become, in relative terms, over super saturated (ie taken beyond the limits set by the tables/PDC) - if appropriate action is not taken.

Bühlmann's Half-time Spectrum

Tissue #	Half-time (min)	Range	Tissue Type
1	4.0		Blood
2	8.0		Brain
3	12.5		Spinal cord
4	18.5		
5	27.0		
6	38.3		
7	54.3		
8	77.0		Skin
9	109.0		
10	146.0		
11	187.0		Muscle
12	239.0		
13	305.0		
14	309.0		Joints
15	498.0		
16	635.0		

Fig 2.7

3. The gas tension in a tissue should never exceed approximately twice the ambient pressure

Even before Haldane, in 1878 Paul Bert, Paris, thought that excess nitrogen was the probable cause of compressed air illness. It was also thought - quite wrongly - that the illness was caused by the *difference* in pressure between the nitrogen inside the diver's body and that outside.

Haldane proved this idea to be incorrect. After many diving excursions under pressure, he showed no incident of bends and was able to bring his subjects directly to the surface provided they went no deeper than 33ft/10m. Haldane also discovered that this was possible, irrespective of bottom time, within the range of his experiments (Modern research has shown this to be too deep and the limit is more like 20ft/6m ie 1.6:1). However, if divers went deeper than 33ft/10m and then rose straight to the surface, they could be expected to display some symptoms.

Haldane's further experiments showed that it was possible to bring a diver up from 100ft/30m to 33ft/10m, or from l65ft/50m to about 66ft/20m, without any problems, irrespective of bottom time.

The crucial point is the change in absolute pressure (in Atm/bars). Each pressure change is shown as a ratio of 2:l, see Fig 2.8.

From this, Haldane deduced that the vital factor governing compressed air illness was not the difference between internal nitrogen tension and external nitrogen pressure, but the *ratio* between absolute pressures at different depths. Provided the ratio of 2:l was not exceeded, he said that there was no danger of compressed air illness.

On this premise - that to exit the water following a dive no tissue compartment in the diver's body must exceed the 2:l pressure ratio - Haldane constructed his tables.

Haldane's 2:1 Ascent Pressure Change Ratio

Safe Ascents		Absolute pressure change	
From	**To**	**From**	**To**
33ft/10m	Surface	2bar	1bar
100ft/30m	33ft/10m	4bar	2bar
165ft/50m	66ft/20m	6bar	3bar

Fig 2.8

He worked on the basis that the tissue compartment first approaching the 2:I pressure ratio barrier, acts as the controlling tissue determining whether or not the diver may exit to the surface without stopping He also saw that according to this ratio a 30ft/9m dive has no limit on bottom time. With modification, (now thought to be less than 20ft/6m) this principle is still used as a basis of many decompression diving tables today.

However, it was discovered that the 2:I pressure ratio was not a magical number for all tissues. For instance, fast tissues (those with short half-times) could withstand more than the 2:I ratio while some slower tissues could stand less.

During the 1930s, decompression research was predominantly being undertaken by the the US Navy. During 1935 they had determined that each particular tissue half-time was associated with a particular unique decompression ratio. By 1937 the decompression ratios were reduced because they were based on dives involving exercise at depth.

In I956, the US Navy issued its new tables, based on the idea of unique decompression ratios for each of the tissue compartment. Also, by this time, it had been determined that these decompression ratios are depth-dependent. Furthermore, the new tables employed a 120 minute half-time tissue, which is much longer than had been considered by Haldane.

M-values (Maximum values)

Although not difficult, the calculations required for the above mentioned system were very tedious and because there were no computers available in those days, prone to error. In 1965 consideration was given to the method of calculation. It had already been suggested that the tissue/ambient pressure differences could be used in place of ratios. But it was not clear if there was any real advantage. However, Workman investigated and came to the conclusion that calculations could be reduced to a series of straight-line graphs, see Fig 2.9, of the form:

$$M = M_0 + a \times D$$

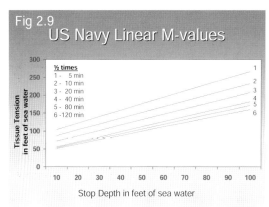

Fig 2.9
US Navy Linear M-values

½ times
1 - 5 min
2 - 10 min
3 - 20 min
4 - 40 min
5 - 80 min
6 -120 min

Stop Depth in feet of sea water

Where "M" is the Maximum value of supersaturated nitrogen for a given depth (measured in feet of sea water), M_0 is the tissue compartment tension (in feet of sea water) allowed at the surface directly after a dive ie the surfacing M-value, "a" is the slope of the graph and "D" is the dive depth in feet (Remember, this was 1965).

This was a very important development and the system has come to dominate thinking ever since. The system is simple to use and has allowed subsequent researchers to fit their data to this straight-line format.

Adopted by the US Navy, Workman's system operated directly in feet of sea water to allow stoppage depths to be matched to the maximum dive depth. Since most navies work at sea-level, this works well.

While Bühlmann, a Swiss medical professor, working in Zurich needed to account for altitude, his system is calibrated in pressure (bar).

Fortuitously this straight-line analysis lends itself very nicely for use in personal decompression computers (PDCs).

Fig 2.10
US Navy & PADI M_0-values

Tissue Half-time (min)	US Navy 1957	PADI (RDP) 1987
	(M_0-values in feet of seawater)	
5	104	102.9
10	88	84.1
20	72	67.2
30	--	59.8
40	58	44.7
60	--	51.4
80	52	49.9
120	51	46.9

In 1987, PADI determined their own set M_0-values. These are compared in Fig 2.10 with those of the US Navy Tables. Lower M_0-values tend to produce more conservative bottom times and therefore potentially safer tables. It is interesting to note that as well as using lower M_0-values than the US Navy, the PADI's Recreational Dive Planner has extra tissue compartments. Furthermore, surface intervals are calculated using the 60 minute tissue compartment instead of the 120 minute compartment used by the US Navy.

Bühlmann's M$_0$-values converted to feet and metres from bar		
Tissue Half-time (min)	M$_0$-value in feet of seawater	M$_0$-value in metres of seawater
4.00	102.30	31.00
8.00	72.89	22.08
12.5	60.81	18.08
18.5	51.96	15.74
27.00	46.23	14.01
38.30	39.86	12.08
54.30	35.49	10.82
77.00	32.44	9.89
109.00	30.21	9.21
146.00	27.99	8.53
187.00	26.24	8.00
239.00	24.70	7.53
305.00	22.83	6.96
390.00	22.04	6.72
498.00	20.79	6.34
635.00	19.84	6.05

Fig 2.11

Fig 2.11 shows Bühlmann's tissue spectrum and M$_0$-value in both feet and metres of sea water.

These lower M$_0$-values promote an even safer system with good repetitive dive options. The longer half-times are not important to recreational divers for the first dive of the day, but they play a significant role in the second and subsequent dives. They are even more important for divers who fly after diving.

Haldane stated that dives to 30ft/9m are not dangerous provided that they are not followed by deeper ones. By inspection of Fig 2.11, it can be seen that Bühlmann has set the safe no time limit depth at about 20ft/6m.

Short bottom times and multiple ascents

Recent incidents, however, have shown Haldane's belief to be false on occasions: In 1989, commercial divers who had been carrying out diving on fish farms around the coast of Scotland suffered a surprisingly high incidence of decompression illness. It was particularly unexpected because their dives were short and shallow.

Typically, these divers descended to between about 16ft/5m and 33ft/10m in fish cages. They spent around five minutes at the cage bottom, then returned to the surface, climbed over to an adjacent cage and repeated the operation. Following a series of four dives to about 39ft/12m and two to 16ft/5m in this pattern within a twenty four minute period, one diver was treated for neurological CNS decompression illness. Similar reports have been received from Finland. Although it has not been proven, it would seem that these incidents are related to the number of relatively fast ascents made which caused bubbles to be generated (free gas) and therefore would not be attributable to bottom time/gas loading.

Recent evidence indicates that bubbles can form directly in the fatty insulating sheath (myelin) that surrounds nerve fibres (axons) in the spinal cord. Myelin protects the nerve fibres in much the same way as the insulation sheath of an electrical cable. If the sheath breaks down, the nerve fibres can be damaged. So, in this way, blockage of blood vessels is not a necessary factor for decompression illness.

It is also known that micro-bubbles can form during an ascent of as little as 23ft/7m! Even more recently, the minimum depth shown to produce micro-bubbles is about 13ft/4m. A number of agencies worldwide now accept that the safe no-limit bottom time depth is about 20ft/6m. However, this does not apply if followed by deeper dive(s) within a 24 hour peroid.

Reverse dive profiles

The above advice on forward dive profiles was to some degree turned on its head by a conference in 1999 at the Smithsonian Institution. However, the conclusion of the meeting seems to be based more on a gut feeling than scientific fact and flies in contravention of a number of papers read at the meeting and of advice offered at other times, ie by Walder '67, Yount '76 and Wienke '98.

For decades all training agencies have insisted upon divers planning forward profile diving. Therefore, the accident statistics reflect this fact. Of course a number of divers have broken this rule and got away with it. Equally, a number of divers have exceeded the no-stop limits without ill effect. The point is that a mass change in dive depth sequence may be dangerous.

Advice on dive depth sequences, Saw-tooth and Yo-yo dive profiles, as well as the maximum number of ascents that can be made during one diving day are given on page 6-12.

4. Decompression should be initiated by a relatively large drop in ambient pressure

Decompression practice prior to Haldane was to haul the

A simplistic construction of a Haldane decompression schedule

Fig 2.12

A 20 minute dive to 30metres (100ft)

Half-time	No. of periods	% Saturation	Tissue PN₂ (bar)	Max ceiling (or stop depth) PN₂ (bar)	Max ceiling (or stop depth) Depth (feet)
5	4	93.75	2.96	1.48	28.82
10	2	75.00	2.37	1.185	16.50
20	1	50 Tissue not at risk	1.58 Tissue not at risk	0.79	Surface
40	0.5	Tissue not at risk	Tissue not at risk	0.79	Surface
75	0.25	Tissue not at risk	Tissue not at risk	0.79	Surface

© Bob Cole

A schedule taken from Haldane's tables as issued by the Royal Navy 1943

TABLE I, SHOWING ORDINARY TIME-LIMITS IN DEEP WATER, STOPPAGES DURING ASCENT AIR SUPPLY NEEDED DURING WORK—*continued.*

DEPTH. FEET.	DEPTH. FATHOMS.	PRESSURE POUNDS PER SQUARE INCH.	TIME UNDER WATER, *i.e.,* FROM SURFACE TO BEGINNING OF ASCENT.	STOPPAGES IN MINUTES AT DIFFERENT DEPTHS. 60 FEET.	50 FEET.	40 FEET.	30 FEET.	20 FEET.	10 FEET.	TOTAL TIME FOR ASCENT IN MINUTES.
96–108	16–18	42½–48	Up to 5 mins.	—	—	—	—	—	3	6
			5 to 10 mins.	—	—	—	—	—	5	8
			10 to 15 mins.	—	—	—	—	3	5	11
			15 to 20 mins.	—	—	—	—	4	8	15
			20 to 25 mins.	—	—	—	1	5	10	19
			25 to 30 mins.	—	—	—	3	7	10	23
			30 to 35 mins.	—	—	—	4	8	13	28
			35 to 40 mins.	—	—	—	5	10	15	33

Fig 2.13

unfortunate diver up from depth, irrespective of bottom time, at the steady, slow rate of twenty minutes per Atm/bar.

Once Haldane had devised his 2:1 pressure ratio, he proposed that decompression should be initiated by a relatively large drop in ambient pressure. According to his system, the diver should be hauled up at the rate of one foot every second (60ft/18m per minute), to a level where the controlling tissue was at - or about - its 2:1 pressure ratio. At this point the diver's ascent would be stopped for a predetermined time to allow excess nitrogen to be eliminated. An example of Haldane's theory is shown in Fig. 2.12 which illustrates a dive of twenty minutes to a depth of 100ft/ 30m.

Clearly, in this case, the five minute tissue is the controlling factor, and a stop would have to be made at ten metres (33 feet).

The schedule below in Fig 2.13 is taken from Haldane's table as issued by the Royal Navy in 1943.

This is an extremely conservative schedule and as we now know is very unlikely to give rise to DCI symptoms. Haldane, however, found it difficult to convince some people that this was the way forward. But convince them he did and compared with the other diving methods of the time, the dreaded bends almost became a thing of the past.

Beyond Haldane

Ever since Haldane's 1908 paper, people all over the world have been trying to improve on his work. Even now, the complete answer has yet to be found and, at the moment, the world does not have a universal first principle theory. It seems that we shall have to be content with small improvements here and there. It is like the days when people thought the earth was flat. Navigators then stayed within sight of land and were able to go about their business successfully despite the fact that their movements were based on false assumptions.

Similarly, divers have not yet discovered the true shape of their decompression world so they have to stick to the safe limits of our knowledge.

Efforts will always be made, in both the commercial and naval diving worlds, to go deeper for longer with the shortest decompression time possible. Time is money and decompression time can cost mega bucks.

Very little time has been spent looking after the sport diver and even less on the gender difference. Sport divers have had to follow, and still do follow, military and commercial developments. As a result longer bottom times and shorter rise and decompression times have come into widespread use and these are now giving cause for concern in the sports world.

The M-values used in the US Navy's decompression tables produce a significant amount of micro-bubbles. This is particularly true if the allowable bottom times are used to the full.

In recent years, however, much has been done by Bühlmann and others to improve decompression efficacy for the sport diver by reducing bottom times, slowing the ascent rate and fitting in safety-stops. However, the grand solution is still not in sight.

That's not to say, however, that sport divers can't do more to protect themselves. The remainder of this book is concerned with explaining about the physics and physiology associated with current thinking and strategies to help avoid DCI in a sport diving setting.

Chapter 3
Physiology and Gas Movement

Introduction

This chapter sets out to discuss the influences on human physiology caused by diving. It is only by describing these processes, in basic terms, that an understanding of how decompression models (algorithms) are applied by the designer of personal decompression computers (PDCs) to the issues at hand. Additionally, it seeks to enhance the diver's motivation to dive within the limits of the PDC being used, and provide the wherewithal to implement the necessary behavioural and environment strategies into the dive plan for safer diving.

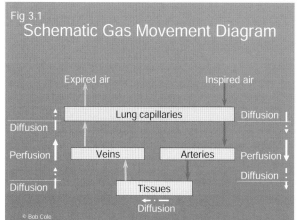

Fig 3.1
Schematic Gas Movement Diagram

Expired air   Inspired air

Lung capillaries   Diffusion

Diffusion

Perfusion   Veins   Arteries   Perfusion

Diffusion

Diffusion   Tissues

Diffusion

© Bob Cole

Gas movement

Gas movement throughout the body holds the key to appropriate decompression. This movement is affected by physical and physiological processes, the environment and diver behaviour.

The need for oxygen to support life goes without saying. Oxygen is drawn into the lungs by the act of breathing, see Fig 3.1, and diffuses through the lung wall where it combines to form a loose chemical bond with the red blood cells (haemoglobin) to become oxy-haemoglobin. The speed of this reaction is extremely fast (ie nanoseconds). Once the bond is made no further oxygen will be admitted, even when the pressure (ie depth) is increased.

Nitrogen also diffuses into the blood, not chemically but in simple solution in accordance

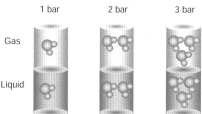

Fig 3.2
Henry's Law
as pressure increases more gas dissolves into a liquid

1 bar   2 bar   3 bar

Gas

Liquid

with Henry's Law; see Fig 3.2, and the quantity of nitrogen loaded is affected by pressure (ie depth).

This gas mix, along with other trace gases in solution, is transported by blood flow (perfusion) to the body's tissues where the oxygen is used (metabolised) to convert food into energy. At normal surface conditions the nitrogen within the body is at balance with the external atmosphere, so there is no net exchange of this gas.

The Oxygen Window

One might expect the tissue tension of oxygen within the body to be equal to the atmospheric value of oxygen, or that the internal tension of all the gases would at least balance with the outside world. But this is not true: at the surface, there is difference in internal gas tension of somewhere between -10% to -15% lower. The first oxygen pressure drop from 0.2bar to 0.13bar occurs in the deep lungs; see Fig 3.3. From the lungs the oxygen diffuses into the arterial system, at the same tension, and is then transported by perfusion to the tissues. Once it has diffused into the tissue, oxygen is metabolised to release energy from food eaten. As a result carbon dioxide is produced as a waste-product (ie an exhaust gas, just like an automobile). This conversion does not reduce the total volume of gas within the tissue, however, it does reduce the tissue gas tension. This is because carbon dioxide is about 21 times more soluble than oxygen and, for a given of quantity of gas, creates less tension, see Fig 3.4 which show how the internal tension changes with depth.

Fig 3.3 The Oxygen Window
Schematic Circulation Diagram

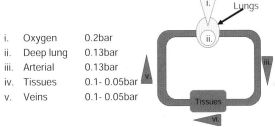

i.	Oxygen	0.2bar
ii.	Deep lung	0.13bar
iii.	Arterial	0.13bar
iv.	Tissues	0.1- 0.05bar
v.	Veins	0.1- 0.05bar

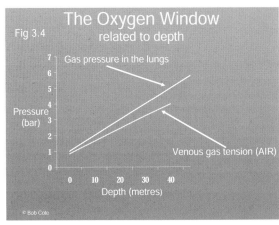

Fig 3.4 — The Oxygen Window related to depth

© Bob Cole

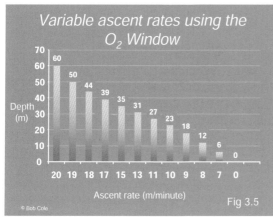

Variable ascent rates using the O₂ Window

Fig 3.5

Depth (m) axis: 70, 60, 50, 40, 30, 20, 10, 0

Bar values: 60, 50, 44, 39, 35, 31, 27, 23, 18, 12, 6, 0

Ascent rate (m/minute): 20 19 18 17 15 13 11 10 9 8 7 0

© Bob Cole

Note: pressure refers to free-gas and tension refers to dissolved gas in tissues. The units are the same, and in this book are given in bar.

The beauty of this is that it reduces the tissue gas tension* to something less than the ambient pressure*. This difference is called the "Oxygen Window", and as previously stated is between -10% and -15% of ambient surface pressure. Furthermore, because the uptake of oxygen is a chemical reaction unaffected by pressure, the "Oxygen Window" widens with depth, see Fig 3.4. Fig 3.5 shows the variable distances between different depths allowed when using the oxygen window to the full, without tissue and venous gas tension exceeding the ambient pressure. This is called the zero-saturation method.

To create free-gas (bubbles) in the body, the tissue gas tension needs to be greater than the ambient pressure (Henry's Law). So the true value of the Oxygen Window is in the fact that a diver can ascend some distance through the water before the tissue gas tensions become equal to the ambient pressure. Typically, this ascent could be about four metres at a depth of 30metres and about two metres at a depth of 10metres, note the Oxygen Window narrows as the depth is reduced, even with Nitrox, see Fig 3.4. To take advantage of this benefit, ascents must be slow enough to allow venous nitrogen in solution to be exhaled in sufficient quantity, via the lungs, to prevent a tissue gas tension overload. The fly in the ointment that spoils Henry's Law in the human body is that micro-nuclei ([†]naturally occurring gas seeds) may allow free-gas to form before the ambient pressure is exceeded thus reducing the protection of the Oxygen Window. This means that all ascents need careful control to maintain the number of bubbles and total volume of free-gas below the critical DCI trigger point.

[†]*A personal thought: A source of gas for these seeds may be Nitric Oxide (NO) which is a naturally occurring free-gas created by the immune system and used to fight infection.*

These tissue compartments are mathematical representations of areas or regions in the body and are not real body tissues.

Tissue compartment tension tolerances (M-values)

During his experiments Haldane, as previously explained, determined that all tissue compartments have a supersaturation nitrogen tolerance of about 2:1, that is the tissue gas

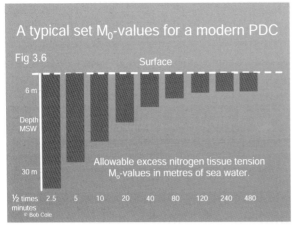

A typical set M_0-values for a modern PDC

Fig 3.6

Surface

6 m

Depth
MSW

30 m

Allowable excess nitrogen tissue tension
M_0-values in metres of sea water.

½ times   2.5   5   10   20   40   80   120   240   480
minutes
© Bob Cole

tension can be allowed to rise to twice the ambient pressure before free-gas is formed. Later, others found that the 2:1 ratio could be increased for fast tissue compartments, but needs to be reduced for the slower ones; see Fig 3.6.

In the sample of allowable excess nitrogen tensions shown in Fig 3.6, it can be seen that the maximum-value (M-value) of nitrogen tension varies from tissue to tissue. So-called fast tissue compartments withstanding a higher M-value than slower compartments.

Fast compartments have a good blood flow into and out of the region (ie the brain, see Fig 3.7) and slower compartments have poorer blood supply (ie joints). For this reason, fast compartments are thought to be more bubble resistant that the slower ones. This is not the only occasion where the speed of reaction plays a role:

Distribution of Blood (cardiac output) during Rest and Work

Source: A A Bühlmann

Fig 3.7

Tissue/organ	Weight (kg)	Blood supply (l/min/kg body weight)		Oxygen consumption (ml/min)	
		Rest	Work	Rest	Work
Brain & spinal cord	01.7	0.50	0.50	40.0	40.0
Kidneys	00.3	4.00	3.00	20.0	20.0
Heart	00.3	0.70	2.00	25.0	25.0
Stomach/intestines/spleen. Liver	04.0 01.5	0.80	0.60	65.0	65.0
Skin	04.0	0.08	0.20	10.0	30.0
Skeletal muscles	30.0	0.04	0.40	60.0	2000
Fat	12.0	0.03	0.04	05.0	10.00
Joints & bones	12.0	0.03	0.06	15.0	25.00
Remainder, incl blood and lungs	09.2			10.0	145.0
Total	75.0			250.0	2500

© Bob Cole

Analogies

- When you are doing the washing up and your wife says to you that there's a spoon missing and you should look for it in the washing up water; if the water is hot you can retrieve the offending spoon without scalding your hands provided that you are very quick. However, if you are allowed to let the water to cool a little, you will be able to search for longer and not get hurt.

- Electrical engineers will tell you that in the case of electric shock, if the "touch" voltage is high, then the safe exposure touch-time must be extremely short. On the other hand if the touch voltage is, say, less than 50 volts the exposure touch-time may safely be extended to minutes without the risk of harm.

These maximum-values (M-values) are used as a means to control safety-stop bottom times, in which case they are called M_0-values (ie M zero-values). This is achieved by terminating the dive when the first tissue compartment (called the "leading compartment") of the set reaches its defined limit. Once into stage-stop diving, it is more than possible that multiple compartments will exceed their limit (M_0-value) for free access to the surface. It is then that the slowest compartment with the smallest M_0-value, which is at or above its M-value, sets the minimum stop depth (or glass ceiling).

The current trend is to reduce M_0-values, which will shorten safety-stop bottom times, in the hope that this will reduce the production of micro-bubbles after the dive. In doing so, this produces the added benefit of improved bottom times for subsequent dives.

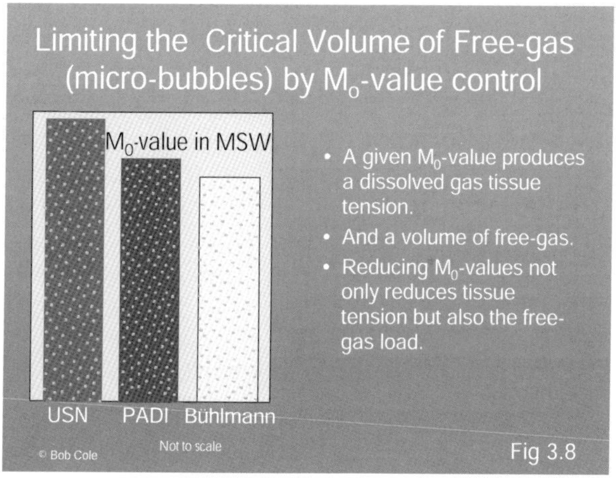

Limiting the Critical Volume of Free-gas (micro-bubbles) by M_0-value control

M_0-value in MSW

• A given M_0-value produces a dissolved gas tissue tension.
• And a volume of free-gas.
• Reducing M_0-values not only reduces tissue tension but also the free-gas load.

USN   PADI   Bühlmann

Not to scale

© Bob Cole

Fig 3.8

It would seem that for a given M_0-value there is a concomitant level of micro-bubbles. The size of bubbles formed depends upon the quantity of dissolved gas. Reducing M-values, particularly at the faster end of the spectrum, reduces the propensity for excessive bubbling, see Fig 3.8.

Tissue compartment half-times

Haldane was also obliged, for the sake of simplicity, to limit the number of theoretical tissue compartments used in the algorithm to five.

Why "theoretical tissue compartments" and not just tissues? Well take the example of a heart, it has:

• Muscle
• Valves

- Nerves
- Blood vessels
- Skin (pericardium)

In fact the heart wall has several different layers of material, so it becomes difficult to identify a single element called a "tissue" and an algorithm is only a theoretical model of the body.

Clearly, there are more than just five tissues in the body and this along with the constant 2:1 M-value may be the reason for the limited success of Haldane's system on long exposures. Since then, in an attempt to fine tune their own algorithms, others have tended to increase the number of compartments used: US Navy - six compartments, PADI - eight compartments and Bühlmann 16 compartments with 16 separate critical tolerance (M-values). The truth is that even this may not be enough to accurately describe the human body. It is, at best, a broad-brush attempt to simplify the modelling problems to achieve an acceptably safe solution. This system is bound to have limitations and will, inevitably, fail from time to time.

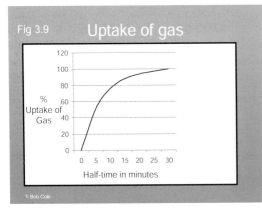

Fig 3.9 Uptake of gas

The idea of half-times is bound up in the concept of blood flow (perfusion) and that the circulating blood will deliver nitrogen to the tissues, in an exponential fashion. Each visit of the blood will fill the tissue a little more until it is full ie equilibrated with the ambient pressure, see Fig 3.9. All PDC algorithms treat perfusion as the dominant factor to the exclusion of diffusion.

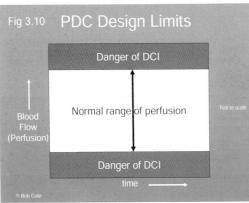

Fig 3.10 PDC Design Limits

The problem here is that perfusion is not constant, with perhaps the exception of the brain, and will vary to match the diver's behaviour and environmental conditions. In general, designers of PDC algorithms assume a maximum and minimum rate of perfusion throughout the dive, see Fig 3.10. If the diver moves outside this range there is an increased risk of DCI.

The dynamic cardiovascular system

The volume of blood circulating is far less than the volumetric capacity of the cardiovascular system.

In the average 70kg person there is between five and six litres of circulating blood; whereas, the cardiovascular system volume (ie heart, arteries, capillaries tissues and veins) when fully opened up could be 150 litres. The obvious question is: why? Clearly if the system can hold 150 litres it must connect to tissues requiring that amount of blood. If that were true all the time, then the heart would need to be the size of a soccer ball to cope with the necessary workload.

Nature is nothing if not ingenious. Certain organs like the brain require a constant supply of blood, whereas that required by muscles is variable and depends upon exercise (workload). To meet the changing needs of the system the body diverts (shunts) blood to the most urgent need, whilst leaving the brain fully supported. In the average person exercising muscle may require up to ten times the amount of blood than when resting, so extra blood is diverted to meet the need.

The skin acts as both a radiator and an insulator; releasing heat when required by increasing blood flow to the surface. It acts as an insulator during cold weather by restricting blood flow (up to -83%) to maintain the body's core temperature.

In other words the cardiovascular system is dynamic and automatically adjusts itself to meet the needs of the individual under a very wide range of circumstances. This dynamic ability can easily be viewed by looking at the palm of your hand where you will be able to see this shunting taking place. Often there are parts of the palm that are pink and parts that are white. The pink parts are receiving blood and the white parts are not. Given time you will see change the taking place, pink goes white and white goes pink as the need alters, see Fig 3.11.

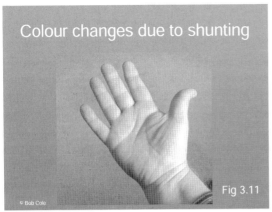

Colour changes due to shunting

Fig 3.11

© Bob Cole

It is difficult to photograph the shunt in the hand, checkout your own hand.

Blood flow (perfusion) can also be disturbed by alien influences, ie free-gas (bubbles) containing mostly the inert make-weight gas of the breathing mixture being used ie nitrogen and/or helium. For divers the introduction of free-gas into the cardiovascular system is quite common, for most dives create micro-bubbles (sometimes called silent-bubbles); which, provided they are kept very small in size and few in number are merely washed to the lungs (pulmonary filter) where they become trapped and slow the elimination of dissolved gas until they themselves dissolve away. However, if the volume of free-gas increases too much this will alter tissue characteristics: slowing half-times and reducing tolerance values, thus increasing the risk of DCI.

You can now see some of the complications that defy the PDC and table designer. Success in achieving safe decompression is limited by how well designers are able to model the human body and its dynamics. Furthermore, success is also dependent upon the diver understanding these issues and how well dive plans are adjusted to cope with these limitations. Remember, this is a risk sport and there are no guarantees.

Other major factors

In addition to the above mentioned variables there is the question a "Patent Foramen Ovale" {PFO or a hole in the wall (septum) of the heart}. In 1901 Fawcett quoted that 28.3% of his sample had a PFO. Today, doctors still say that between 25 and 30% of the general population have this condition in varying degrees of severity.

Why does this condition exist? Before birth the fetus has a modified circulation because the placenta is doing the job of the fetal lungs, intestines and kidneys. Therefore, the patent foramen ovale (PFO) and patent ductus arteriosus (PDA), see Fig 3.12, work together to greatly reduce the

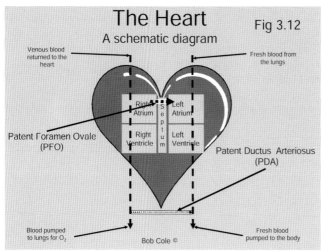

The Heart

A schematic diagram

Fig 3.12

Venous blood returned to the heart

Fresh blood from the lungs

Right Atrium

Septum

Left Atrium

Patent Foramen Ovale (PFO)

Right Ventricle

Left Ventricle

Patent Ductus Arteriosus (PDA)

Blood pumped to lungs for O_2

Bob Cole ©

Fresh blood pumped to the body

Note: *In real life the PDA connection is above the heart and between the pulmonary artery and the aorta.*

[1]**Important:** *Medical research has shown there is link between Migraines, particularly migraines with aura (ie flashing lights), and PFOs.*

blood supply to the lungs of the fetus. At birth these "shunts" are supposed to close and seal. Some do not.

In the case of PDAs and large septum defects, doctors take appropriate corrective action. In a number of cases the PFO defect is small and goes unnoticed. In the non-diver this is not life threatening; although some people may not feel as well as they might and may suffer from [1]migraines. For the diver with a PFO the risk is greater.

In the normal heart blood is pumped from the right ventricle to the lungs where gas exchange takes place. However, the lungs have another major function: due to the small diameter of the capillaries they act as a filter, catching debris flowing in the blood and preventing it from being washed into the arterial circulation. For the diver this is a blessing, because the lungs or so-called "pulmonary filter" also trap free-gas (micro-bubbles) preventing it from being delivered to major organs: brain, spine, liver etc. A PFO is a by-pass (shunt) that can circumvent the lungs allowing micro-bubbles into the arterial circulation to cause arterial gas embolism (AGE) or cerebral gas embolism (CAGE).

Micro-bubbles

Most of the blood that flows through the lungs is involved in gaseous exchange with the outside world. However, a small proportion of blood is used to supply oxygen to the fabric of the lung tissue itself, and when used it flows into the arterial circulation without giving up its CO_2 or other gases. This is called admixing. At rest, say in the armchair, when cardiac output is low admixing is in the order of between 5% and 10%. When working, the volume of admixing remains the same but the percentage drops as cardiac output increases.

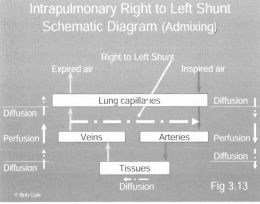

When diving admixing may increase and become an important issue.

Following most dives, returning venous blood carries with it microbubbles (MBs). These MBs are normally washed to the lungs (the so-called pulmonary filter) where they become trapped until the free-gas within the bubbles dissolves back into the blood and is then eliminated in the normal way. During the time in the lungs these MBs reduce the lung surface area and therefore the nitrogen washout rate. Furthermore, they restrict normal blood distribution causing an increase over normal admixing of venous blood with arterial blood (a right to left shunt occurs across the lungs: called an "intrapumonary right to left shunt") and nitrogen rich blood is caused to re-circulate, see Fig 3.13.

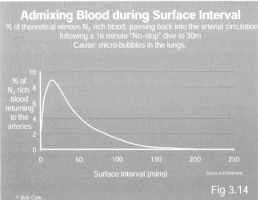

Cardiac output at rest is about 5.7l/min. During hard work it rises to around 17.3l/min.

For example, Bühlmann in Switzerland showed that a 16-minute dive to 30 metres causes a 9% shunt, see Fig 3.14. This is at a time when cardiac output is greater than sitting in an armchair. This admixing delays nitrogen off-gassing and if not accounted for in the PDC algorithm increases the risk of DCI. Furthermore, the MBs in the lungs pose a risk of wash-through into the arterial circulation during subsequent dives, particularly if they are deeper than the previous dive. Contrasting the 16-minute 30 metre safety-stop dive with a 25-minute 40 metre stage-stop exposure we find an interesting 5% reduction in the admixing blood, see Fig 3.15.

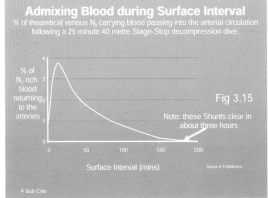

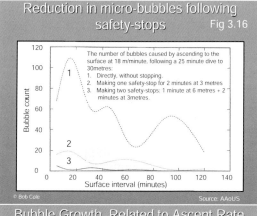

Reduction in micro-bubbles following safety-stops   Fig 3.16

The number of bubbles caused by ascending to the surface at 18 m/minute, following a 25 minute dive to 30metres:
1. Directly, without stopping.
2. Making one safety-stop for 2 minutes at 3 metres.
3. Making two safety-stops: 1 minute at 6 metres + 2 minutes at 3 metres.

Bubble count (vertical axis), Surface interval (minutes) (horizontal axis)

© Bob Cole   Source: AAoUS

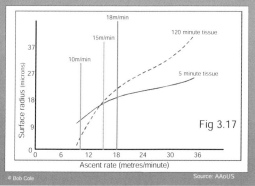

Bubble Growth Related to Ascent Rate

Surface radius (microns) (vertical axis), Ascent rate (metres/minute) (horizontal axis)

18m/min, 15m/min, 10m/min, 120 minute tissue, 5 minute tissue

Fig 3.17

© Bob Cole   Source: AAoUS

Note: For the sake of clarity in Fig 3.17 only two tissue compartment curves are shown.

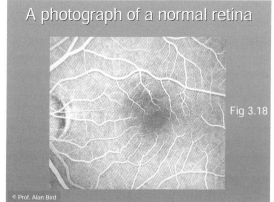

A photograph of a normal retina

Fig 3.18

© Prof. Alan Bird

This idea was supported by Pilmanis in the USA, see Fig 3.16, when he demonstrated that the micro-bubble count could be reduced to about one fifth by making a safety-stop of just two minutes at three metres and still further reduced by stopping at six metres for one minute and at three metres for four minutes. He also demonstrated, that the speed of ascent affects the radius of the micro-bubbles which form, see Fig 3.17 overleaf. Two powerful statements and a strong incentive to better control ascents.

Other major aspects

i. Carbon dioxide (CO_2)

Carbon dioxide is the exhaust gas produced as a result of the metabolic process. It is carried in the blood in the form of an acid called "bicarbonate". This may be a source of micro-nuclei (gas seed).

Carbon dioxide can also alter blood flow because it enlarges blood vessels (vaso-dilatation). It also contributes to "sludging" of the blood by making the red blood cells become more sticky. It is important to avoid CO_2 retention and maintain the level within the normal range.

ii. Further proof

Further proof of potential damage, if further proof is needed, comes from a 1988 study by Polkinghorne, Sehmi, Cross, Minassian and Bird who looked at lesions in the eyes of divers. Fig 3.18 shows a normal retina, Fig 3.19 shows minor pigment and capillary changes in the eyes of scuba

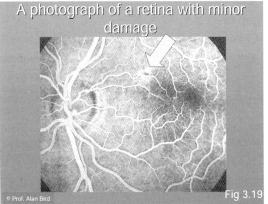

A photograph of a retina with minor damage

© Prof. Alan Bird   Fig 3.19

A photograph of a retina with gross damage

© Prof. Alan Bird   Fig 3.20

Photographs courtesy of Prof. Alan Bird, Institute of Ophthalmology London.

May result in brain damage.

divers and Fig 3.20 shows gross changes in a diver's eye. The findings of the study were statistically significant, it showed that during the first year of diving 22% of the divers surveyed developed pigment changes in their eyes. In divers with no record of DCI, 36% had pigment changes. Whilst in those with a history of DCI 92% had changes. None these divers had any idea that they had suffered any damage - *silent bubbles cause silent damage. In fact, diving could be described as a "slow accident"!*

The authors suggested vascular obstruction (ie blocked blood vessels) as the cause.

Given that free-gas obstructs blood vessels and ascents cause free-gas, it would seem common sense to slow the rate of ascent and include safety-stops.

The eyes are end organs of the brain, and a window into the body that needs no scalpel. Capillary damage seen here is likely to be mirrored in the brain itself.

iii. Temperature

Temperature change affects the uptake of N_2 and the M-value of certain tissue compartments. The blood supply to the extremities of the body ie feet, legs, hands and arms is regulated so as to maintain the body's core temperature at 37ºC. In cold water this means a reduction in perfusion to the extremities. This restriction of perfusion increases still further as the exposure time increases.

The solubility of nitrogen is also affected by temperature and this can have an adverse affect on M-values.

iv. Dehydration

Dehydration may creep up unnoticed, caused by so-called "insensible" water loss: sweating, breathing and evaporation that is not balanced by an appropriate intake of fluid. Normal bodily functions, enhanced by cold, further reduce fluid retention. Under these conditions, the circulation of a dehydrated person is compromised and for the diver may slow the elimination of excess nitrogen after a dive.

v. Alcohol and diving

Alcohol is in fact a poison (albeit, for many people, a nice poison). It acts as a diuretic and makes you pee. This is an attempt by the body to rid itself of the poison. For the diver trying to avoid DCI, this has two outcomes: dehydration and the lowering of the surface tension of the blood. Dehydration has been dealt with earlier. The reduction of blood surface tension makes it easier for free-gas to form.

Basically, drinking alcohol before diving is not an option. Drinking after diving increases the potential risk of DCI.

vi. Anxiety

Our bodies are affected by our emotional state: ie fear increases the flow of adrenaline, which increases blood flow (perfusion). If left uncontrolled, this may move the gas exchange rate outside the range of the PDC being used.

vii. Biochemistry

Decompression illness is not just a matter of the adverse effects of Boyle's Law. It is a complex process that also involves the immune system. It is well known that at a cut on the surface of the skin, blood platelets cause clotting to seal the wound. Similarly, bubbles in the blood also attract the attention of the immune system: Blood platelets aggregate around bubbles and clots can occur.

Recent studies have indicated that bubble formation causes the immune system to activate the so-called "complement" system. This may be responsible for such symptoms as: itching, pulmonary swelling, small blood vessel leakage, increased blood viscosity and much more.

viii. Smoking and gas exchange

Tobacco smoking is the largest preventable cause of death in the world. Causing, amongst other things, lung cancer, heart disease etc. Tobacco smoke contains three main substances: nicotine, carbon monoxide (CO) and tar.

Nicotine is highly addictive and it is thought to increase the stickiness of blood platelets, intensifying the risk of blood clots and potentially causing DCI.

Carbon monoxide (CO) binds with the red blood cells (haemoglobin) and excludes the uptake of oxygen. It does NOT interfere with nitrogen uptake.

Tar is a complex mix of chemicals that paralyses the tiny hairs (cilia) of the lungs. This results in a build-up of mucus that traps dust, pathogens and air. Trapped air at the surface may not cause problems, but for the diver it is potentially dangerous and may result in a burst lung with free-gas entering into the arterial circulation. This is called arterial gas embolism (AGE) and can result in DCI of the brain (CAGE) and/or spinal cord. Not a nice thing.

"Air trapping" may damage the terminal bronchiole of the lungs allowing free-gas to enter the arterial circulation. This may cause DCI in tissues that would otherwise remain bubble free.

Conclusion

Understanding gas movement through the body is important. Perfusion is the key to this understanding, equally it is important to identify the things that assist or impede its flow. The diver must plan the dive taking into account all aspects that may cause perfusion rates to move outside the upper and lower limits set by the algorithm of the PDC being used.

This means assessing work-rate, skin cooling, breathing patterns and micro-bubble generation then adjusting behaviour or the PDC's settings, or both, to accommodate for the additional risk.

Chapter 4
Women and decompression

Introduction

Very little research and even fewer facts - no real changes in 1996

It's a sad fact but true, that there has been very little research done with regard to women and diving in general, and decompression illness in particular. This is because almost all research has either a military or commercial importance, and there are very few women diving in these fields.

However, an increasing number of women are becoming involved in scientific studies underwater. Diving under these conditions is only a means of getting to and from the work site and is secondary to the main purpose - research - and, as in sport diving, decompression research has been very limited.

One survey in the US by Dr Susan Bangasser 1978, indicated that those women who responded had 3.3 times greater incidents in suspected or treated decompression illness compared to men. However, there were only 649 respondents.

A survey conducted in Britain regarding men and women divers - well worth reading!

Previous finding in doubt

More recently in 1994 the Diving Diseases Research Centre (DDRC), Plymouth, England published their report on a respective study involving some 2,250 divers, 46.67% (1050) of which were women. The report entitled "Men and Women in Diving" is 117 pages long and it is not possible in this book to do it justice. However, in view of the size of the population capture Bangasser's results seem high. The DDRC report covers 450,827 dives reported by 2,222 divers after 28 spoiled survey forms were removed. There were 87 cases of DCI reported, 50 men and 37 women. This raw data gives a DCI incident per 1000 dive of 0.157 for men and 0.262 for women. When adjusted for years of diving experience the figure is higher for men. The report also noted that men are "more aggressive" (adventurous) in their diving than women. They do more diving and more decompression dives than women. Perhaps the DCI incident rate is linked more to the type and frequency of diving than gender.

A long term study between 1987 and 1997 by Diver Alert Network (DAN) indicates that overall, DCI accidents are becoming less frequent. During the period, they examined about 500 DCI incidents per year. This is thought to represent about half of all the reported incidents. DAN reported an incident rate of 0.04% which suggests that diving is a relatively safe sport. It seems that about two thirds of all DCI cases involve the central nervous system (CNS). However, the number of serious cases involving paralysis or losing consciousness has dramatically reduced. The proportion of women divers, over the period, has increased from 24% to 31%

Patent Foramen Ovale (PFO)

Since becoming identified as a predisposing factor for DCI, the Patent Foramen Ovale (PFO) seems to be cropping up more regularly. This may be because people are now looking more closely for them. In 1901 Fawcett reported "that it may possibly occur more frequently in the female than the male". In any event DCI from this cause is still relatively rare, for treatment see chapter 6 page 6-21.

Physiological differences

Theoretical increased risk of DCI

In general, women have a greater proportion of body fat. This has two immediate effects: more weight is needed to correct for positive buoyancy and more importantly, since fatty tissues have a greater affinity for nitrogen than say muscle, a greater gas burden accumulates during a dive of equal depth and duration compared to men. This theoretically enhances the risk of decompression illness, but has not been proven. In fact, the 1994 DDRC survey failed to identify any connection between DCI in the overweight male or female sport diver.

What is fat anyway? Well, I think that it applies to anyone who is fatter than the author!

The idea that fat people are more likely to suffer a DCI hit comes from studies of caisson workers who were exposed to high ambient pressures for long periods (8 hours shifts) and were working during this time. It could be that the relatively short exposures and low work rate of sport divers helps protect them in this respect.

Menstrual period

Around and during the menstrual period a woman may suffer from oedema - fluid retention - this theoretically makes her slightly more susceptible to decompression illness; although this has not been proven.

Dehydration and premenstrual stress may reduce tolerance

If a woman can tolerate vigorous exercise during menstruation, she should be able to dive without problem. However, there may be an increased risk of decompression illness due to dehydration and premenstrual stress may make some women more accident prone and some may have reduced tolerance. In general, whether or not to dive during these times is dependent on how the woman feels.

Recording the menstrual cycle

Improving your own records will help determine if there are any links between DCI and the MC

The DDRC report makes great stress on the fact that most women divers do not accurately record their menstrual cycle (MC). Because of this, it is impossible from their collected data to determine if there is a link between the DCI incident rate and the MC. They conclude that if women want better information on this topic they will need to keep accurate records of their own MC.

Keep your MC records with your diving log book

These records will be of little use if they are not available to the attending doctor at the time of any DCI incident - for better use they should be kept with the diver's log book.

Oral contraceptives

The effects of the birth control pill are not well documented

The effects of oral contraceptives relating to diving are not well documented. There has been speculation that the older type of pill can cause micro-sludging in the circulation. However, the newer pills used now have a lower dosage and are not generally thought to cause this problem. Although a theoretical risk of DCI exists, their use alone does not appear to be a problem.

Pregnancy

Inappropriate oxygen level may damage unborn baby

Many women dive during the early weeks of pregnancy while conception may still be unsuspected, at the time when the fetus is particularly vulnerable to deformation or so-called "teratogenic" influences. It is important that the fetus gets the right level of oxygen - neither too little nor too much.

There is speculation that intravascular "silent" bubbles, while not large enough to cause decompression illness in the mother, may restrict fetal or placental blood flow; thus reducing oxygen flow.

Intravascular silent bubble trouble not proven

Part of the treatment for decompression illness is to recompress the victim to about three bars and administer 100% oxygen. If the victim is pregnant the high pressure oxygen could be either lethal or teratogenic to the fetus.

Potential danger to the unborn child from the mother's therapeutic recompression treatment

It also appears that pregnant women may retain more residual nitrogen compared with non-pregnant women.

Nitrogen retention

Any woman who is trying to conceive or knows she is pregnant should ask herself before diving: "If anything goes wrong and either I lose the baby or it is born damaged, how will I feel?

Holiday diving and spontaneous abortions

From the 'free-form' response section of the questionnaire DDRC have identified a potential risk of spontaneous abortions. However, this was a very small number of women and the rate was about the national average.

The report said *".... When we investigated the outcome of the pregnancies where 'holiday' style diving had taken place we observed that four, out of the five respondents of spontaneous abortions in this group, had taken part in consecutive day diving. ...."* they were in the early stages of pregnancy and unaware of this fact at the time of diving. Accurate MC records may help avoid this problem.

Better MC records required

Recommendations

There is very little hard experienced knowledge in this area and the advice given is usually to err on the side of caution, particularly where an unborn child is concerned.

It is recommended that any woman who is trying to conceive or knows she is pregnant should refrain from diving.

Refrain from diving

In my book "Decompression and Computer Assisted Diving", before the DDRC study, advice was given on shallow water diving ie 30ft/9m or less. In view of some of the

Previous advice withdrawn!

women's comments taken from the "free-form" section of the DDRC survey, I can only withdraw my previous limitations and advise that it seems unwise to dive when you are pregnant or when you are trying to conceive. Additionally, because of the high oxygen content of Nitrox it would appear to be potentially more hazardous for the unborn child than air.

Nitrox diving - don't even think about it!

If alleviation of menstrual symptoms requires prescription analgesics, then the victim should refrain from diving while using them.

Don't dive when using analgesics

Diving after childbirth

There are no set rules to say when a new mum may start diving again after giving birth.

Not without your doctor's agreement - 2nd opinion may be required

Caution is of the utmost consideration and therefore no diving should take place without the agreement of your family doctor - who may need to take advice from a hyperbaric specialist.

Chapter 5
Personal Decompression Computers

Background

The idea of personal decompression computers (PDCs) is not new. In 1951 the US Navy formed a committee for undersea Warfare and Underwater Swimmers. Its purpose was to act as a think-tank to identify diving equipment improvements for Scuba divers. In 1953 the committee issued a report (Groves and Monk 1953). This report contained a design for the "Ultimate Gauge" which was an electrical analogue computer. The design called for the device to incorporate both decompression and air consumption data. A very tall order, and one that would take decades of work to fulfil.

The Foxboro Decomputer Mk1
Circa 1955

Fig 5.1

Nevertheless, in 1955 Foxboro had produced a decompression meter which they submitted to the US Naval Experimental Diving Unit (NEDU) for consideration. It was a pneumatic two tissue compartment analogue device based on the Grove and Monk report, see Fig 5.1. After due consideration the NEDU rejected it because it was not completely compatible with the US decompression tables of the time.

It was the amateur sports diver who first benefited from a commercially produced PDC. This single tissue compartment analogue PDC designed by Carlo Alinari was produced by the Italian company "SOS" of Torino, and was called Automatic Decompression Meter (or D.C.P.), see Fig 5.2. The makers claimed extraordinary reliability: . . . "For single or multiple

DCP handbook circa 1960

Fig 5.2

dives, where the first decompressing level is no greater than 15m (50ft), THE AUTOMATIC D.C.P. is infallible." . . .

The Automatic DCP was a single tissue compartment device that used an enclosed flexible bag that connected to a bourdon tube with a pointer on a scale, via a gas permeable ceramic plug. As the diver descended, gas from the flexible bag was forced through the permeable ceramic plug into the bourdon tube which moved the pointer to indicate the required decompression.

The performance of the Automatic DCP device was based upon the sixty minute half-time tissue compartment as used in the then new (1957) US Navy decompression tables. This was a true analogue personal decompression computer, which followed the diver's progress both underwater during the dive and during the surface interval. Thousands of sports divers around the world relied upon the Automatic DCP. The device was still in production as late as 1991.

Others were also trying, with mixed results, to develop a safe PDC. In the early 60s Texas Instruments produced the "Tracor" which used an electrical network of resistors and capacitors to model the transport of gas through the body. It was rejected by the NEDU as unreliable due to temperature variations. Others who tried their hand include: General Electric, Farallon (Oceanic), DCIEM, Dacor. Unlike the Italian Automatic DCP most of these were so-called table-followers, which tracked the diver's progress against an inbuilt set of tables.

The break-through did not come in a single move; it required the development of reliable temperature-stable pressure transducers and low power consumption micro-processors that could be made waterproof and pressure proof.

The Big Shake-up

The sport was given a wake up call when in 1983 two separate manufacturers; one in the US and the other in Switzerland, marketed their electronic digital PDCs that for the first time calculated the diver's decompression obligation by integrating depth (partial pressure N_2) over real-time during the dive.

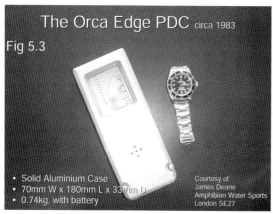

The Orca Edge PDC circa 1983

Fig 5.3

- Solid Aluminium Case
- 70mm W x 180mm L x 33mm D
- 0.74kg, with battery

Courtesy of
James Deane
Amphibian Water Sports
London SE27

Fig 5.4

The Deco-Brain I PDC circa 1983

Marketed as the Hans Hass Deco-Brain

About the size of a house brick   A modern PDC

The US company was Orca Inc that produced the "Edge" PDC which utilised a US Navy based algorithm modified by Dr M P Spencer's "silent bubble" (micro-bubble) research. This in effect reduced M-values as a means of limiting silent bubbles, see Fig 5.3. The Swiss company Divetronic AG marketed the "Hans Hass Deco-Brain I", which employed Professor Dr A A Bühlmann's 16 tissue compartment ZHL12 algorithm, which also had a measure of micro-bubble control, see Fig 5.4.

Interestingly, both devices used a maximum ascent rate of ten metres per minute which was extraordinarily slow by the standards of the day. This seemed to set a trend of slow ascending that moved through the sport to good effect. Nowadays much is made of the virtues of ascending slowly.

An overview of PDCs

When used correctly, modern PDCs give a more accurate assessment of the diver's current theoretical nitrogen loadings. As a result, the PDC may allow the diver more dive time compared to the traditional square profile table system; because they are able to compute and re-evaluate the theoretical nitrogen levels, ie uptake and elimination, constantly throughout the dive (with sample rate of one to three seconds), giving the diver more freedom through multi-level dive calculations. This would be impossible using traditional square dive profile assessment with conventional tables.

PDCs come in a wide range of designs, and new developments are taking place all the time.

How do PDCs work? In principle they are simply very fast

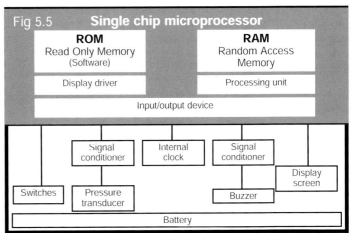

A block diagram showing the various generic components of a PDC.

adding machines that are able to follow a predetermined set of rules called an algorithm, to calculate the theoretical movement of inert gas (nitrogen in most cases) in and out of the diver's body. In real terms, however, they are very complicated devices and since this book is not intended as a computer manual, the following is only an overview of the structure and operation of common types of PDC.

In general PDCs have nine main components, see Fig 5.5: the power source (battery); the pressure transducer; an analogue to digital converter (signal conditioner); a microprocessor, the read only memory (ROM) and the random access memory (RAM), an internal clock, a thermometer and the screen display.

The power source (battery) must provide sufficient power to support the needs of the other components. Some PDCs allow the user to change the batteries, while others do not.

Battery life in modern PDCs is relatively long, whichever method of installation is used, and depends mostly on the usage of the PDC; although with wet type contacts the degree of maintenance (ie not cleaning off salt) may have an adverse bearing on battery life.

Once switched on, most PDCs follow a self-checking program. As part of this program, in some PDCs, the pressure transducer (electronic pressure gauge) measures the ambient pressure as a reference for the following dive. Some PDCs continuously monitor atmospheric pressure, even while not in use.

The function of the pressure transducer is to convert pressure into an electrical voltage (the so-called analogue form). This voltage is converted by the signal conditioner into digital form for use by the microprocessor. This information is used along with digital time information from the internal clock to perform the mathematical and logic operations required by the decompression algorithm.

The PDC's microprocessor has two types of memory: ROM and RAM. The ROM is a permanent memory which contains the decompression algorithm as well as other constants such as the sampling rate (which tells the PDC how often it should calculate the decompression status), the number of tissue compartments and their half-times, M and M_0-values. It also tells the microprocessor which steps it needs to take and the order in which to take them. The RAM is where dive data and calculation results are stored.

Unlike "Standard" diving (ie surface supplied air, copper helmet, heavy twill suit and lead boots etc) Scuba diving, using decompression tables, is multi-level diving but treated as square-profile diving. Whereas PDC diving is truly multi-level. The modern PDC splits dives into a series of "mini-dives" of between one and three seconds in duration (depending upon the make and type of PDC), see Fig 5.6. They then calculate the nitrogen uptake/elimination for each of these mini-dives and summate them together to give the decompression status. With this system a 40 minute dive could be sub-divided into 800 mini-dives, each needing its own set of calculations. For a PDC with six tissue compartments such a dive would involve 4800 exponential calculations. During the surface interval the calculation frequency is reduced to around ten minutes, as there are likely to be fewer pressure changes and they will be small in value.

A multi-level dive profile

Fig 5.6

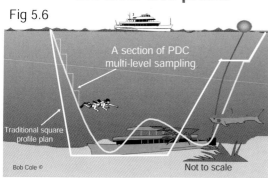

A section of PDC multi-level sampling.

Traditional square profile plan

Bob Cole ©   Not to scale

The internal clock determines the dive time and the surface

interval. It also provides a time base for the microprocessor calculation rate. Nowadays, many PDCs offer the diver a time and date display.

The display screen is the diver's window on the theoretical nitrogen loadings or decompression status and obligation. Typically, the display will show current depth, maximum depth attained during the dive and other information such as total ascent time, decompression ceiling, ascent rate, ascent rate violation, missed stops and surface interval.

Current Developments

Since about 1983/4 there has been a tendency to reduce M and M_o-values in the hope that this will reduce the production of micro-bubbles. If followed to the nth degree these values could be reduced to such a ridiculous level as to prevent practical diving. There is a need to do some more thinking. There are five parts to a dive that can be controlled:

- Rate of descent
- Bottom time
- Rate of Ascent
- Stops
- Surface interval

Rate of Descent

Very few systems set a maximum rate of descent. The general consensus, by table designers, is to include descent time in the bottom time. This has caused some table users to descend with all possible haste. On the other hand PDCs chop the dive, including the descent, into mini-dives of one to three seconds and integrate the uptake/elimination of nitrogen to each tissue compartment to determine the decompression obligation. It would seem reasonable to think that the rate of descent may make a contribution to the decompression outcome, much in the way it affects nitrogen narcosis. Something for the future? Perhaps!

Bottom Time

Bottom time (BT) is determined by the partial pressure of inert gas N_2 or He (depth) related to the time of exposure and the design M/M_o-values, see Fig 5.7.

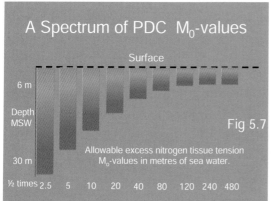

A Spectrum of PDC M_0-values

Surface

6 m

Depth
MSW

30 m

Fig 5.7

Allowable excess nitrogen tissue tension
M_0-values in metres of sea water.

½ times 2.5   5   10   20   40   80   120   240   480

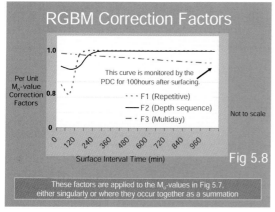

RGBM Correction Factors

1.0

Per Unit
M_0-value
Correction 0.8
Factors

This curve is monitored by the
PDC for 100hours after surfacing.

··· F1 (Repetitive)
— F2 (Depth sequence)
– · F3 (Multiday)

Not to scale

0

0   120   240   360   480   600   720   840   960

Surface Interval Time (min)

Fig 5.8

These factors are applied to the M_0-values in Fig 5.7,
either singularly or where they occur together as a summation

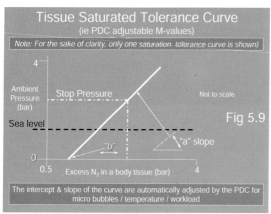

Tissue Saturated Tolerance Curve
(ie PDC adjustable M-values)

Note: For the sake of clarity, only one saturation tolerance curve is shown

4

Ambient
Pressure
(bar)   Stop Pressure   Not to scale

Fig 5.9

Sea level

"b"   "a" slope

0

0.5   Excess N_2 in a body tissue (bar)   4

The intercept & slope of the curve are automatically adjusted by the PDC for
micro bubbles / temperature / workload

Most PDCs seem to leave it there. However, a small number view this as a starting point, or maximum allowable BT, to be modified by the diver's behaviour and environmental conditions. The diver's behaviour has three factors:

- the profile itself (yo-yo and saw-tooth)
- skin cooling
- Work-rate.

Yo-yo and Saw-tooth Dive Profiles

Bottom times for yo-yo and saw-tooth dive profiles may be modified by this type of PDC, which adjusts M/M_0-values (and in some PDCs the associated half-time) in real-time during the dive to reduce the exposure or to introduce stops in an attempt to safely deal with the production of micro-bubbles. Fig 5.8 shows the reduced gradient bubble model (RGBM) correction factors that are applied to relevant tissue compartments to track behaviour and reduce the M_0-values shown in Fig 5.7.

Fig 5.9 (linear M/M_0-values) shows an alternative system that simultaneously increases half times and reduces M/M_0-values of relevant tissue compartments to deal with micro-bubble production thus tracking behaviour (Note: for clarity only one curve is shown).

Skin Cooling

Some researchers conclude that exposure to cold water also has an effect on gaseous exchange. With this in mind one PDC manufacturer has introduced an automatic skin-temperature adaptive algorithm that adjusts skin half-times and M/M_0-values simultaneously as required, see Fig 5.9. The PDC considers the exposure time and temperature, and adapts the decompression obligation if necessary. Other manufacturers fit personal adjustment factors, reducing M/M_0-values, that can be selected by the diver according to their own assessment of the situation.

Work-rate

Many manufacturers settle for modest M/M_0-values as a catch-all solution to all situations. The truth is that blood perfusion to muscles increases during times of exercise. If this exercise causes excess delivery of nitrogen to the working muscles, then extra decompression time may be required for its elimination. Traditionally, decompression table rules ask the diver to make an assessment for work-load and to feed that information into the dive plan. Check your own tables system for the rules.

However, one PDC maker measures the diver's air consumption to assess work-load. The information gathered is fed into the algorithm, which adjusts both the muscle half-times and M/M_0-values simultaneously as necessary, see Fig 5.9. Other manufacturers offer diver selectable personal adjustment factors as a means of dealing with the problem: these adjust the M/M_0-values.

Ascent rates

Ascents of all types can affect micro-bubble production and most manufacturers deal with this by using a constant slow ascent rate. This is all well and good provided the diver is able to comply. Life is often less than simple and mistakes occur; to cope with these little surprises some manufacturers employ an ascent violation compensation algorithm. This is in general achieved by adjusting M/M_0-values, see Fig 5.9 and in one particular case by adjusting half-times as well, see Fig 5.8.

Continuous Decompression

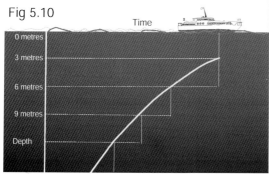

Fig 5.10

Some researchers believe that progressive decompression is better than stepped decompression.

In his 1908 paper, Haldane set the standard for decompression stops at 10 foot (3 metre) intervals. This has, it seems, been transcribed in tablets of stone. In Haldane's day, divers were suited and booted with very heavy weights and air was pumped down to them. Their depth and rate of ascent was controlled by attendants on the surface pulling on a connecting rope. Free divers do not have the luxury of this type of ascent control. Nonetheless, the ascent rate and stop depths are dominated by this concept. Equally, Haldane did not have the benefit of computers and micro-processors. One PDC manufacturer has recognised that advantage may be taken of the micro-processors functionality and has adopted a "continuous" decompression, ie their PDC has no predetermined (fixed) decompression stop depths until the three metre level, see Fig 5.10. This functionality has also been used to inform the diver when the "decompression floor" is reached, ie a point above which the leading tissue compartments are off-gassing and decompression stop time does not increase. It is worth noting that at or about the actual floor off-gassing is slow, because of the small gradient.

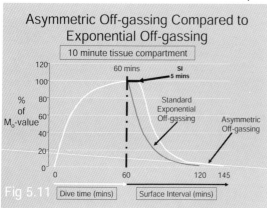

Fig 5.11

Surface Intervals

During surface intervals the majority of PDCs simply follow the fixed out-gassing rates of the various tissue compartments, in an exponential way. Some employ an asymmetric out-gassing system ie the out-gassing rate is slower than the in-gassing rate, see Fig 5.11. This helps, to a degree, with minor micro-bubbling. While the better class of PDC act additionally on modifying M/M_0-value or half-times and

M-values according to diver behaviour and environmental conditions. Latterly, some PDCs acknowledge that micronuclei (naturally occurring gas seeds) are excited into a higher energy plane and require attention for about 100 hours after surfacing, see Fig 5.9.

Choosing a PDC

There are, in general, three types of divers buying PDCs, those who:

- want the best advice.
- know exactly what to buy.
- don't care which PDC they buy, as long as it gives the longest bottom time!

Be very careful of PDCs that extend bottom times without appropriate decompression stops because they are potentially more dangerous.

There is a plethora of PDCs on the market and more arriving by the week. Choosing the right PDC needs careful thought: examine your diving needs, both current and future. If you're not currently a Nitrox diver, look around your club to see what the trend is, this may help you decide. Don't be too coy about Nitrox, it's becoming very popular and may be used to extend bottom times without creating decompression stops. Furthermore, Nitrox PDCs can be used for air diving and are very often no more expensive than air PDCs.

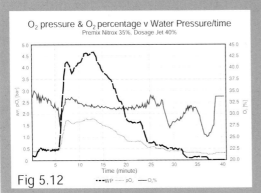

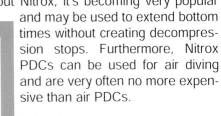

O$_2$ pressure & O$_2$ percentage v Water Pressure/time
Premix Nitrox 35%, Dosage Jet 40%

Fig 5.12   ---WP ····· pO$_2$ —O$_2$%

Dive Logs

All PDCs have a facility to download information into a PC from a previous dive. However, some PDCs cannot download into an Apple-Mac.

Dive profiles stored in a PDC, and viewed via a PC, are a very useful way of examining exactly what happened during a dive, see the example in Fig 5.12 of a semi-closed circuit rebreather dive.

What style of PDC?

Would you prefer a wristwatch type that you can wear to the office? Often these have smaller faces, so would you feel better with a normal wrist mounted type PDC? This type can also be mounted into a console. You might like to consider an air integrated model that also tells not only your cylinder pressure but also your remaining air time (at your current depth and work rate).

In any event consider PDCs that use an automatic micro-bubble control algorithm and a means of adjustment for workload and cold water which can be either manual or automatic.

Chapter 6
DCI avoidance strategies

Introduction

The outcome of any dive is affected by many factors. This chapter offers a number of strategies to help protect the diver against DCI. The actual cause of DCI is unknown. What is known however, is that free-gas is always present in DCI casualties, but that DCI is not always present when bubbles exist. This makes giving advice very difficult. Accepting advice may help protect you. You will never know. On the other hand, ignoring such advice is not a guarantee to cause DCI. The beast is very fickle.

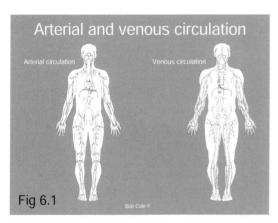

Arterial and venous circulation

Arterial circulation

Venous circulation

Fig 6.1

Bob Cole ©

The general consensus is that DCI is very likely following fast ascents and often when decompression stops are missed. The best advice possible is to avoid those factors that are thought to increase the probability of DCI. The three main contenders are:

- Excess exercise (work load)
- Skin cooling
- Micro-bubble (free-gas) generation

The human body is a very complicated maze of arteries, capillaries, venules, veins etc, see Fig 6.1. For the purposes of this book anatomically correct drawings are too intricate. All that is needed is a simplified appreciation of the facts in decompression model terms, see Fig 6.2. *Note: There is no heart shown in this diagram, this is because it's a drawing of a Diving Officer!* Even the exact detail of this drawing is not entirely necessary, you

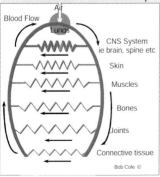

A Schematic Diagram of the Circulation and Body Tissues. Shown As Simple Water Pipes

Blood Flow

Air

Lungs

CNS System ie brain, spine etc

Skin

Muscles

Bones

Joints

Connective tissue

Each body tissue is represented by a water pipe to demonstrate the blood-flow & half-time:-

large short pipes for fast body tissues with a good blood supply and short half-time;

thinner longer pipes for slower body tissues with poorer blood flows and longer half-times.

Fig 6.2

Bob Cole ©

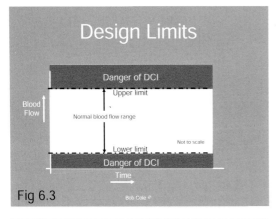

Fig 6.3

just need to remember that "fast" tissue compartments are depicted by a short wide-bore pipe and that "slow" tissue compartments are shown by long narrow-bore pipes.

Decompression algorithms work on the assumption that blood perfusion will be maintained within a maximum and minimum limit, see Fig 6.3. If perfusion is altered such that it moves outside these limits, the risk of DCI increases.

Work Load

From earlier chapters you will know that the uptake of inert gas (Nitrogen, Nitrogen & Helium and on its own Helium) follows the exponential form and that the speed of uptake is governed by the tissue half-time, see Fig 6.4 uptake curve, with % uptake v time. Tissue compartment half-times are a measure of blood perfusion.

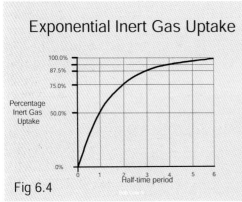

Fig 6.4

Perfusion is not a constant and will vary for most tissues according to diver behaviour and environmental conditions. Exercise increases blood flow to the working muscles. This is to bring the much needed oxygen. The down side is that it also brings the inert gas with it. During a dive there might be, say, three levels of perfusion:

Changing Workload Underwater

• Muscle tissue at a light work rate (load) - normal blood flow (perfusion) and gas uptake.

• The same muscle tissue at high work rate - high perfusion and high gas uptake. Blood flow could be increased by up to 750%.

• Now at rest, say during a safety-stop, blood vessels return to normal. Extra time is needed at the stop level to let the additional nitrogen wash-out!

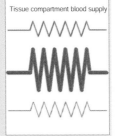

Tissue compartment blood supply

Fig 6.5   Bob Cole ©

• general swimming,

• digging out that bar of gold

• and the decompression stops.

Clearly, during the work phase the perfusion rate is much higher than

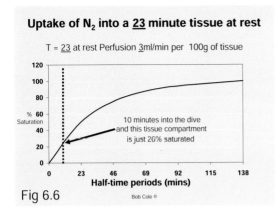

Uptake of N$_2$ into a <u>23</u> minute tissue at rest

T = <u>23</u> at rest Perfusion <u>3</u>ml/min per 100g of tissue

10 minutes into the dive and this tissue compartment is just 26% saturated

Half-time periods (mins)

Fig 6.6

Bob Cole ©

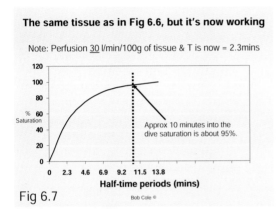

The same tissue as in Fig 6.6, but it's now working

Note: Perfusion <u>30</u> l/min/100g of tissue & T is now = 2.3mins

Approx 10 minutes into the dive saturation is about 95%.

Half-time periods (mins)

Fig 6.7

Bob Cole ©

during the rest of the dive, see Fig 6.5. If the work element of the dive is significant, ie in excess of the upper design limit, then extra stop time will be required.

As an indication, Fig 6.6 gives a graphical comparison between a working and a non-working muscle. The graph in Fig 6.6 assumes light work and that after ten minutes at the operating depth the tissue compartment is loaded to 26% of its M-value. If, due to exercise, the perfusion rate increases by a factor of ten then the tissue compartment half-time (T) will reduce, see Fig 6.7. The graph now shows the compartment saturated to 95% of its M-value, in the same amount of time.

This example shows the need to take account of exercise during the planning stages of the dive. There are two basic strategies that can be used:

Estimate the level of work likely to be done during the dive. This is not that easy! What is considered to be work in excess of algorithm design limits? Few designers provide this information. However, Albert Bühlmann did. His tables and PDCs are designed on the assumption that an average work load would cause an oxygen consumption of about one litre of oxygen per minute on the surface. In round terms this represents a respiratory minute volume (RMV) of about 23 to 25 litres of air per minute per bar. From the graphs produced by Lanphier, an averagely fit person would consume a litre of oxygen when swimming at a mean speed of 0.6 knots (ie about 20 metres per minute).

RMV assessment

It is no bad thing for divers to know their RMV, but in the case of estimating work load to help prevent DCI it becomes very important.

Using the above information a diver could get a handle on this issue by a trial swim in a local swimming pool. The method is very simple:

- use a scuba with a small dive cylinder (this will produce less of an error because of the large pressure drop).

- swim a defined distance in a specified time; say 200 metres in about 10 minutes at a constant depth.

- at the end of the trial swim; record the actual distance covered in metres, the time of the swim in minutes, and the cylinder pressure drop in bar.

- note how you feel at the end of the swim, this should give you a muscle memory for future use.

To calculate your RMV use the following formula:

$$RMV = (WC \times Pd/Pab) \div t \text{ (min)}$$

Where:

- WC = the water capacity of the dive cylinder (litres).
- Pd = the pressure drop cause by the trial underwater swim.
- Pab = the absolute pressure at the underwater swim depth.
- t = the time in minutes taken to make the trial underwater swim.

Example:

Depth of swim:	3 metres
Distance:	200 metres
Time taken for the swim:	9 minutes
Cylinder WC:	3 litres
Cylinder WP:	232 bar (start pressure)
	140 bar (at the end of the test)
Pressure drop (Pd):	$P_1 - P_2$) 232 - 140 = 92 bar

$$RMV = \{(3 \times 92) \div ([3/10] + 1)\} \div 9 = \textbf{23.6 litres/min/bar}$$

Average swimming speed=

$$200 \text{ m} \div 9 \text{ minutes} = \textbf{22.2 metres/min}$$

This RMV assessment can be used in dive plans to help evaluate the need for extra time at the stop depth.

Dive planning

Fig 6.8
PDC setting guidelines

Type of Dive	Level of conservatism
Pefing dives	Default or factory setting
Heavy swimming Mild N-fME (ie 1 porthole)	First level of adjustment
Prolonged heavy swimming Heavy N-fME (ie 2 porthole)	Second level of adjustment

Bob Cole ©

All dive tables have rules that must be applied when the diver is involved in work during the dive. This usually means planning the dive as if it were one whole depth increment deeper than the actual depth; ie a 30 metre dive should attract the decompression obligation of a 33 metre dive. The actual rules for the specific tables used must be followed implicitly.

If the dive planned is a photographic/exploration/fish watching (Pefing) type dive that turns into a non-ferrous metal excavation (N-fME) dive, extra decompression time may be required. This is where the muscle memory from the above mentioned RMV assessment comes in; because you will know how it feels at the upper breathing limit of the tables, which warns you of the extra decompression need.

Adjustments for a 30 metre dive

Level of conservatism	Bottom time (min)
Default or factory setting	18
First level of adjustment	14
Second level of adjustment	12

Fig 6.9   Bob Cole ©

There seems to be no such rules provided with PDCs. However, some PDCs have buttons that allow the diver three levels of decompression conservatism. The settings shown in Fig 6.8, although not absolute, can be used as a guide. A reasonable range of bottom times for a 30 metre dive is shown in Fig 6.9.

Setting a PDC to say the first or second level of conservatism does not preclude a diver from, in this case, completing an 18 minute bottom time. It will, however, oblige the diver to make decompression stops on the way back to the surface.

The third way to deal with the underwater work load issue is to use a gas integrated PDC that can modify the algorithm on the fly in real-time during the dive. This book is not about selling PDCs, or for that matter any other dive equipment, so no advice is given about makes and/or models of PDC. The reader needs to be aware that not all gas integrated PDCs can handle work load. On this matter seek advice from your local dive store.

Pre-dive and Post-dive Exercise

Pre-dive and post-dive exercise has been shown to increase the quantity of free-gas in the body.

Pre-dive exercise is thought to stimulate pre-existing micro-nuclei (naturally occurring gas seeds that exist in all people) to an increased state of excitation: so-much-so that there is an increase in the number of micro-bubbles after diving.

Post-dive exercise on the other hand increases the potential of converting micro-bubbles into full blown DCI-bubbles. This is possibly because exercise increases the perfusion rate which may cause the blood to vortex, thus creating areas of negative pressure into which excess nitrogen and micro-bubbles can aggregate. Equally post-dive exercise, including snorkelling which can cause bubbling, should be restricted as much as possible at least for the first three hours after exiting the water, which is when micro-bubbling reduces to almost zero, see Fig 6.10 and Fig 3.15.

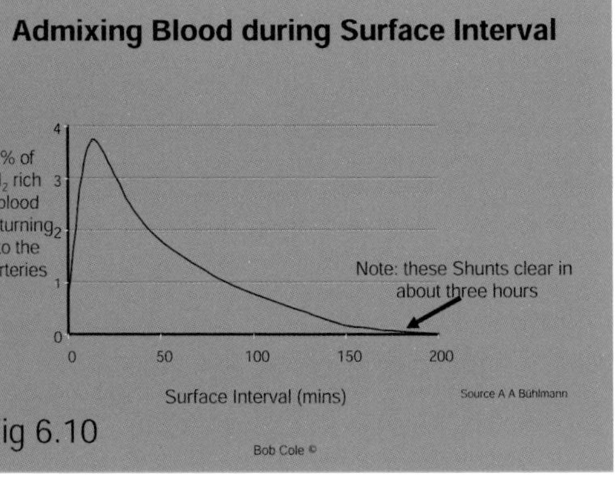

Temperature

Changing work-rates is only one of the ways to alter blood perfusion rates. Altering the ambient temperature also affects perfusion rates, as the body tries to maintain its core temperature at a constant 37°C.

Admixing Blood during Surface Interval

% of N_2 rich blood returning to the arteries

Note: these Shunts clear in about three hours

Surface Interval (mins)

Source A A Bühlmann

Fig 6.10

Bob Cole ©

During hot weather the skin acts as a radiator, dissipating heat by opening up blood vessels and allowing in extra blood to take internal heat to the surface.

In cold weather and in cold water the body progressively closes down the blood supply to the peripheries ie hand, feet and skin. This is to reduce the heat loss, via the blood, to the outside world and to reduce the amount of cold blood delivered back to the core.

Pre-dive cooling

It is important to keep warm before the dive, so appropriate clothing is essential. Furthermore, the diver needs to take account of Wind Chill. The following table gives an idea of the cooling effect of the wind, see the Wind Chill Factor Table Fig 6.11.

Fig 6.11
Wind Chill Factor Table

Wind speed (Km/h)	Temperature (°C)	Apparent Temperature (°C)	Apparent Temperature Drop (°C)
8	35	33	-2
16	35	21	-14
32	35	12	-23
48	35	5	-30

Bob Cole ©

Dive Assessment/planning

For the diver trying to manage safe decompression in cold water this problem has to be addressed. This perfusion adjustment is time dependent and therefore the restriction increases as the exposure time goes on. During the early section of the dive perfusion is normal, allowing nitrogen to be absorbed. As the exposure increases skin blood vessels start to close down and finally at the end of the dive, during the stops when movement is least, blood vessels may be severely restricted, see Fig 6.12. This may necessitate additional stop time to allow excess nitrogen to be eliminated. In relative terms, ascent and stop times are often very short in relation to the bottom time.

This problem is not confined to the relatively cold water of the UK. Decompression illnesses relating to skin cooling have been reported by American cave divers where the

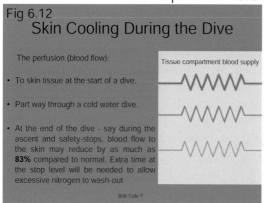

Fig 6.12
Skin Cooling During the Dive

The perfusion (blood flow):

Tissue compartment blood supply

• To skin tissue at the start of a dive.

• Part way through a cold water dive.

• At the end of the dive - say during the ascent and safety-stops, blood flow to the skin may reduce by as much as **83%** compared to normal. Extra time at the stop level will be needed to allow excessive nitrogen to wash-out

Bob Cole ©

Warmth is often over estimated. If you feel cold you are cold. Take appropriate decompression action.

†However, at least one naval trial cast doubt on the worth of Argon as an insulator.

mean temperature is said to be 22°C/72°F. Appropriate clothing is essential. In Finland they say there is no such thing as bad weather, only bad clothing!

For long exposures, †Argon (A) may be used for dry suit inflation in place of air due to its lower thermal conductivity. It is essential to flush the dry suit through with Argon to eliminate the air which, if left in place, will compromise insulation efficiency.

Decompression tables also have rules that must be applied to cold water diving. This also means planning the dive as if it were one whole depth increment deeper than the actual depth; ie a 27 metre dive should attract the decompression obligation of a 30 metre dive. The actual rules for the specific tables used must be followed implicitly.

Fig 6.13
PDC setting guidelines

Type of Dive	Level of conservatism
Reef dive 20°C + (wet suit) English Channel 10°C & above (Dry suit)	Default or factory setting
Below 10°C (Dry suit)	First level of adjustment
Below 7°C (Dry suit)	Second level of adjustment

Bob Cole ©

As with work load adjustment, most PDC manufacturers give no helpful advice. The above mentioned conservatism adjustment may be used for cold water diving. The settings shown in Fig 6.13, although not absolute, can be used as a guide.

Post-dive cooling

For the same reasons as shown in Fig 6.12, it is wise to keep warm after diving. Restricted peripheral circulation may slow nitrogen wash-out to such an extent that inert gas tensions may remain above the design limit for the next dive.

Post-dive sunbathing/hot showers etc

The solubility of nitrogen within the human body is affected by temperature. If the temperature is increased then tissue gas tensions will rise. On the surface, at the end of a dive the diver is supersaturated with nitrogen and provided this supersaturation is within the design temperature constraints of the decompression model, all should be well.

However, if the skin temperature is allowed to rise significantly by say, the diver taking a hot shower/bath or

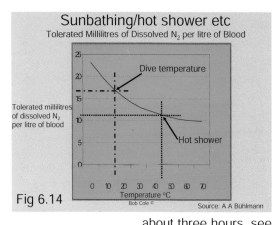

Sunbathing/hot shower etc

Tolerated Millilitres of Dissolved N_2 per litre of Blood

Fig 6.14

Bob Cole ©   Source: A A Bühlmann

sunbathing, then tissue tolerance to gas tension may be compromised and free-gas can form, see Fig 6.14. Hence a normally safe dive can become problematic.

This is another case where surface interval becomes very important. Both Pilismann's and Bühlmann's work become very helpful, because it indicates that micro-bubble production reduces to a relatively safe level following a surface interval of about three hours, see Fig 6.10 and Fig 3.15.

Fig 6.15 **Bubble Dynamics**

° **Micro-nuclei:** naturally occurring "gas seeds" that exist in your body. The numbers are increased by compression/decompression (diving). More micro-nuclei equals potential for more micro-bubbles.

O **Micro-bubbles:** diving grows them from "gas seeds". During an ascent, dissolved nitrogen forms gas around micro-nuclei to create micro-bubbles. Very small bubbles have a high surface tension that tries to collapse the bubbles down.

◯ **DCI bubbles:** out-of-control micro-bubbles that have grown too large.

Bob Cole ©

Blood flow →

A body slice

Micro-bubbles (free-gas)

The current concern is free-gas (bubbles). In simple terms there are three types of bubble:

- Micro-nuclei (naturally occurring gas seeds within the body).

- Micro-bubbles, which may grow from micro-nuclei.

- Full blown DCI bubbles, which may grow from micro-bubbles, see Fig 6.15.

Fast ascents create free-gas (bubbles) in the body!

Diving (ie compression and decompression) is thought to excite micro-nuclei to a higher energy level from which, given the conditions, they progress to micro-bubbles. Most dives produce micro-bubbles. Current thinking is that the body can cope with a small amount of free-gas. If maintained at modest levels, micro-bubbles are washed by the venous blood to the lungs (sometimes called the pulmonary filter) where they become trapped in the small lung capillaries. In this state, the gas within the micro-bubbles becomes isolated from the blood and cannot be eliminated from the body until it diffuses back into the blood.

Diver behaviour

Diver behaviour before, during and after diving may contribute to the production of micro-bubbles. It may be helpful to understand the factors that help resist bubble birth and growth. Nature has provided us with a number of mechanisms that work to resist bubbling:

- ambient pressure.
- tissues (fat/muscle etc) that resist deformation by pressure.
- surface tension of blood.
- the oxygen window helps maintain tissue tension below ambient pressure.

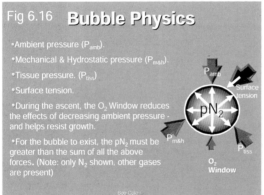

Fig 6.16 **Bubble Physics**

- Ambient pressure (P_{amb}).
- Mechanical & Hydrostatic pressure ($P_{m\&h}$).
- Tissue pressure. (P_{tiss})
- Surface tension.
- During the ascent, the O_2 Window reduces the effects of decreasing ambient pressure - and helps resist growth.
- For the bubble to exist, the pN_2 must be greater than the sum of all the above forces. (Note: only N_2 shown, other gases are present)

Bob Cole

Excluding the effect of micro-nuclei, bubbles can't exist if the tissue tension is maintained below ambient pressure; see Fig 6.16.

Pre-diving activities may cause an increased number of micro-bubbles after the dive. Equally, strenuous exercise after diving may also cause problems. See the section on Pre-dive and Post-dive Exercise above.

During the dive almost any ascent has the potential to create micro-bubbles. It was once thought that bubbles could be avoided by maintaining tissue tensions below their M_0-value and that dives to less than 10 metres (ie 2 bar) had an endless bottom time. Then evidence was produced that the limit was about seven metres. It has now been demonstrated that depths as shallow as four metres can create micro-bubbles.

Really, it is the ascent speed and number of ascents that need to be better controlled. In the early 1990s, fish farmers in Scotland and the Nordic countries were reported to have contracted DCI from dives to five metres and less. It turned out that these guys were cleaning the bottom of the fish keeps. This meant they were making a number of ascents as they worked from keep to keep. Following the rules of their decompression tables they did not exceed or even approach the allowable bottom times for the dive depth attained, yet some divers were hit by DCI. The problem was not the bottom times, but the ascent portion of the dives. Great care is needed to manage safe ascents, see Fig 3.14 regarding safety-stops and Fig 3.15 regarding ascent rate.

Micro-bubbles Fig 6.17

- Micro-bubbles:
  - Disturb blood flow.
  - Alter tissue compartment M-valves and Half-times.
  - Slow gas elimination.
- Tables and most PDCs cannot account for micro- bubble formation.
- Recent research has suggested that micro-bubbles can be formed by an ascent of less than four metres!
  - Older research suggested seven metres!

Bob Cole ©

Micro-bubbles slow gas elimination by restricting blood flow: this alters tissue compartment parameters, see Fig 6.17. In general, no decompression table and many PDCs can not cope with this dynamic situation. Some tables and PDCs have a static element built into the algorithms, but in general it is left to the diver to adopt the correct ascent rate and apply the appropriate safety-stops. The good news is that a number of manufacturers are fitting active on-line bubble control into their algorithms that respond in real-time to the diver's behaviour. If this type of PDC detects a fast ascent or fast ascents it will calculate and apply safety-stops that are in addition to those that would otherwise apply, see Fig 5.8 and Fig 5.9. If you require more incentive to make safety-stops, then maybe Fig 6.18 will provide the evidence. The case is very strong!

Safety-Stops Reduce Fig 6.18
Tissue Tension and Bubble Radius
(12 Minute Dive to 36 Metres, Ascent Rate 18m/minute)

- This table shows the relative improvements in gas tension and bubble radius (micro bubbles or free gas) achieved by applying a one 3 minute Stop at about 4.5 metres (15ft) compared with a direct ascent.
- The researchers who did this work say that this is **almost** as good as halving the ascent rate.
- Standard ascent rate of 10m/minute with a three minute Safety-Stop at 3 metres would be better still.

| | % Relative change | |
Half-time (min)	Tissue tension	Bubble radius
5	-21	-68
10	-11	-39
20	-6	-24
40	-2	-16
80	1	-2
120	2	1

Bob Cole ©

Source information: AAUS

Saw-tooth and Yo-yo dive profiles

The ascent phase of diving can be regarded as a bubble generation process. This is true even if the ascent is not to the surface, ie saw-tooth dive profiles. In the real world this type of profile is difficult or even impossible to avoid. To minimise bubble generation make the rise sections very slow and, where practical, go around and not over rocks etc.

Frequently revisiting the surface - yo-yo dive profiles - is a wonderful way to create free-gas. Safety stops are a good defence and, for the instructor training divers, a very rich Nitrox when coupled with safety stops can do wonders. The best option where possible is avoidance.

Dive depth sequence *(forward/reverse dive profiles)*

As mentioned in page 2-14 the depth sequence of dives may have a bearing on the final outcome.

The 1999 Smithsonian conference concluded that for "*no*-decompression dives" to a max depth of 130ft/40m or less, reverse dive profiles may be conducted provided that the depth differential does not exceed 40ft/12m.

This means that if the first dive reaches a depth of say 33ft/10m the second dive can be no deeper than 73ft/22m and the third dive is limited to 113ft/34m. However, at the time of writing this book the only message on the grapevine was *". . . reverse dive profiles are OK!"* There was no mention of the max depth and depth differential limits.

In the author's opinion there are two reasons to avoid reverse dive profiles. The first reason is, as already mentioned in chapter 2, insufficient evidence to make the change from tradition. Reason two is that micro-bubbles trapped in the lung filter from previous dives may be compressed and washed through into the arterial circulation.

Prevention is better than cure

The general Haldanean concept is that bubbles will not form if the design M_o-values are not exceeded. So to achieve a maximum nitrogen washout in the minimum of time the diver is brought quickly (usually somewhere between 10 and 18 metres/minute depending upon the designers beliefs) to the stop depth to create a large pressure gradient causing dissolved gas to quickly diffuse out through the lungs. This is fine provided there is no free-gas floating around inside the body. This method, however, is in conflict with the idea of bubble control. If free-gas is present an alternative approach is required. When bubbles are small their surface tension is high.

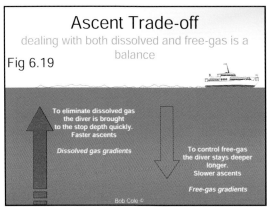

Ascent Trade-off

dealing with both dissolved and free-gas is a balance

Fig 6.19

To eliminate dissolved gas the diver is brought to the stop depth quickly. Faster ascents

Dissolved gas gradients

To control free-gas the diver stays deeper longer. Slower ascents

Free-gas gradients

Bob Cole ©

Furthermore, if these bubbles are kept small, the high surface tension can be used to help collapse the bubbles down. This means slowing the rate of ascent by introducing "DeeP" bubble stops. This is an ascent dilemma, see Fig 6.19. In the real world this becomes a trade-off; a mix of deeper stops and slower ascents. It's not proven, but it seems to work.

The simple notion behind DeeP stops is to reduce the inert gas tension in the leading tissue compartment.

It is thought that reducing the tissue gas tension during the ascent in this way will slow the ascent and keep the pressure on very small micro-bubbles, which have a high surface tension, collapsing them down, even making them go away.

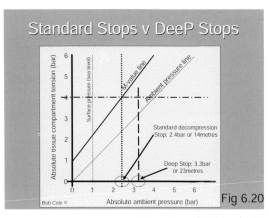

Standard Stops v DeeP Stops

Standard decompression Stop; 2.4bar or 14metres

Deep Stop: 3.3bar or 23metres

Absolute tissue compartment tension (bar)

Surface pressure (sea level)

M-value line

Ambient pressure line

Absolute ambient pressure (bar)

Bob Cole ©

Fig 6.20

The graph in Fig 6.20 illustrates a leading tissue compartment with a gas tension of 4 bar.

Using the standard M-value would allow the diver to ascend to a depth of 14 metres (2.4 bar), which creates a pressure difference (or gradient), internal to external, of 1.6 bar. If instead of using the full allowable M-value the diver elected to halve the difference between the M-value and the ambient pressure, the new stop depth would become 23 metres (3.3 bar). Now the pressure difference is just 0.7 bar, a less stressful situation that provides better bubble control.

In the real world, putting this strategy into action depends upon your method of diving. This system is not for use with standard air or Nitrox diving tables. However, it is workable with both PDCs and custom decompression tables generated with the aid of a personal computer (PC).

With some custom tables the diver is able to dial in a percentage safety factor that adjusts the standard M-values, as mentioned above, to introduce DeeP stops. However, it should be remembered that for example, a 50% safety factor refers to placing the new M-value half way between the standard M-value and the ambient pressure. This does not mean the diver will be 50% safer. To be safe in the use of these systems it would be wise to take training from a qualified instructor.

Most PDCs can not automatically calculate DeeP stops. However, there is a very simple, but crude, method of dealing with the situation. In broad terms the idea is to make intermediate DeeP stops to better control the production of micro-bubbles. This can be achieved by placing the first DeeP stop half way between the maximum depth of the dive and the first formal stage or safety-stop. For example on a dive to say 36 metres where the first formal stage-stop is say 3 metres, the DeeP stop would be at:

(Max. depth - deco stop depth) ÷ 2

(36 - 3) ÷ 2 = 16.5 metres, say 16 metres in round terms.

The aim is to control bubble growth not eliminate dissolved gas. The target is the first two or three tissue compartments that bubble very easily, see curve "1" in Fig 3.16. Therefore, these bubble-stops should only be for about two minutes. I usually apply this method on any dive deeper than 25 metres. On dives beyond 40 metres I repeat the process and add a further DeeP stop before the formal requirement.

In truth, some dissolved gas will be eliminated from the faster tissues and some will be accumulated in the slower ones. The PDC will handle this gas exchange.

The net result on some dives will be slightly longer formal stops and on other occasions formal shallower stops will disappear.

Ascent training

The ascent is potentially the most dangerous manoeuvre of any dive and can cause damage without the diver's knowledge, see page 3-11 "ii. *Further proof* ".

It is very important to give student divers ascent training that will not damage them. One way is to teach students to perform an imaginary ascent on the surface along a rope, ie dry walking the line at the ascent rate.

When you are sure the idea has been grasped and the student can maintain the correct pace, move into the swimming pool.

Set the ascent rope out along the bottom of a swimming pool, deep to shallow end and have the student follow the line at the desired ascent rate (*Done this way, the rate of change in pressure is small and can do no damage*).

When satisfied that the student has mastered the manoeuvre, set the rope vertically in the deep end of the pool and get them to practice real "ascents". When completely satisfied with their skills ability, teach them to make a safety-stop in mid water.

Other factors beyond the Tables and PDCs

There are a number of factors that tend to increase the likelihood of DCI that are outside the control of both Tables and PDCs, see Fig 6.21:

- CO_2 retention
- Dehydration
- Flying before and after diving
- Diving with or after a cold
- Smoking
- Ear clearing
- Blood donation
- Drugs
- Stress
- Obesity
- Patent Foramen Ovale (PFO)

Fig 6.21

PDCs can't check for clean air, that's still your job!

© Charteris

CO_2 retention

Carbon dioxide is a vasodilator, ie it increases the diameter of blood vessels allowing more blood to flow and increase the nitrogen delivered. Poor breathing technique may cause CO_2 retention. This can upset the decompression balance and make DCI more likely. Excess CO_2 may dilate lung capillaries allowing free-gas to pass into the arterial circulation. Avoid skip-breathing (holding your breath to increase air duration) and avoid upper chest breathing. Breath use your diaphragm to pull air down into your lungs, this will provide better ventilation and minimise CO_2 build-up.

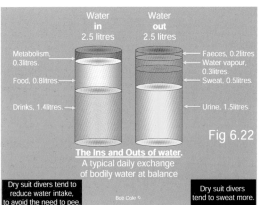

Fig 6.22

The Ins and Outs of water.
A typical daily exchange of bodily water at balance

Dry suit divers tend to reduce water intake, to avoid the need to pee.

Dry suit divers tend to sweat more.

Dehydration

Dehydration thickens or concentrates the blood, which alters blood flow. This in turn interferes with the movement of nitrogen and may lead to unexpected DCI.

The fluid level in the body changes regularly through what is called insensible water loss: sweating, breathing and evaporation. Equally, water is lost in both urine and faeces excretion, see Fig 6.22. To be correctly hydrated simply means balancing fluid loss with fluid intake.

A practical guide is that urine should be almost colourless. Any darker than pale yellow shows that you are dehydrated.

It is worth remembering diving and getting cold will also help expel fluids from your body.

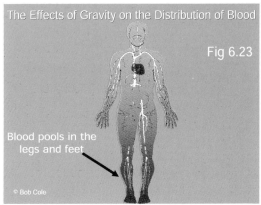

The Effects of Gravity on the Distribution of Blood

Fig 6.23

Blood pools in the legs and feet

© Bob Cole

The effect of gravity that pools blood in the feet and legs, see Fig 6.23, is lost when you are immersed in water. This means extra blood will circulate in the trunk of the body. Nature does not like such inequities and so removes some of the excess by converting part of the blood into urine.

From your training you will know that the body is always trying to maintain its core temperature at a constant 37°C. In cold weather and in cold water the body progressively closes down the peripheries: hands, feet etc in order to reduce heat loss and cooling from returning cold blood. The closing down of blood vessels also increases the volume of blood in the trunk of the body, and as mentioned above some of the excess is converted into urine. From this it can be seen that you will also need to put some water back into your body after diving.

Dry suits may also contribute to dehydration, because even in cold weather they tend to cause sweating, see Fig 6.23. Some dry suit divers hold back on drinking during the diving day to ward off the need to pee, especially when diving from an inflatable boat.

Even in normal life, proper hydration is simply part of a regime to maintain good health. In diving, dehydration may be the straw that breaks the DCI camel's back.

Quenching your thirst on the day is not the same as rehydration. So, it is prudent to ensure that you are correctly hydrated for, at least, three or four days before diving.

Flying before diving

There's not a diver training agency in the world that doesn't make great play on good dive planning and flying after diving.

Very few talk about flying before diving. Flying is another situation that contributes to dehydration; if it's not the dry air of the air-conditioned cabin, then duty free booze will certainly help.

Another factor is fatigue. Research has shown that the fatigued diver bubbles more readily after diving than the relaxed well rested diver.

Make sure you are hydrated and well rested after your flight.

Alcohol and diving

When asked the rules about drinking and diving, some say "It's compulsory!" Dean Martin once said "I'm sorry for anyone who doesn't drink, because that's the best they're gonna feel all day!" Many divers, including me, like a drink. So no preaching!

The main things to know is that alcohol:

- reduces the surface tension of the blood, making bubbling easier.
- is a diuretic, which makes you pee, and contributes to dehydration.
- clouds judgement, and
- the brain remains dehydrated longer than the rest of the body - that is why hangovers last so long.

Moderation is the key word, supported by excellent hydration control. Drinking a tumbler full of water before bed will also help.

Diving after a cold

All diver training agencies instruct firmly that diving with a cold must be avoided. Only a few mention diving after a cold.

Some time ago the Royal Navy had a spate of burst lungs incidents from what was considered to be a quite normal diving operation. Examination of the facts found that a number of the men had had a cold within ten days prior to their accident. These men had mucus in their lungs that caused "air trapping". During an ascent, air in the lungs trapped behind this mucus may not be able to escape in the normal way and is forced through the lung wall into the blood.

To avoid potential lung damage the Navy recommended a ten day break between the end of a cold and diving.

Smoking and diving

As mentioned in chapter 3 smoking has consequences for the diver. Additionally, air trapping (mentioned above) is also a major concern. Avoidance is the best solution.

Ear clearing

The traditional method of ear clearing is the use of

Valsalva's manoeuvre - pinching the nose and blowing to open the eustachian tube. This method is generally used because it is easy to teach. However, it can be unkind on the ear if excessive force is used. Furthermore, it does have the effect of increasing the pressure on the right side of the heart compared to the left. In normal circumstance this is not a problem. But for those with a PFO (a small hole in the heart) micro-bubbles passing through the right side of the heart may be forced through the PFO, by-passing the lungs, into the arterial circulation. This is potentially very dangerous as micro-bubbles could find their way to the brain or spine.

A way to reduce the problem is to:

- use an ear clearing method that does not put extra pressure on the right side of the heart: ie swallowing and wiggling the jaw etc.

- leave a minimum three hour surface interval between dives - see Fig 6.10.

- use Nitrox and decompress using air tables.

Sea sickness

Preparation is the key, if you are prone to sea sickness take your medication early.

If you become moderately sea sick on the boat you can dive, because the sick will stop when you enter the water.

If the sea sickness involves a lot of reaching, diving should be suspended until the next day when you have regained your hydration.

Diarrhoea

Diarrhoea not only causes distress but a loss of essential electrolyte from the stomach. The diarrhoea itself can be brought under control by using a commercially available product such as Aret.

However, the lost electrolyte must be urgently replaced. There are a number of proprietary products on the market that can help in this regard ie Doralyte. If you have no medication, use pure fresh orange juice which is high in potassium.

Blood donation

The giving of blood reduces the donor's blood volume. This will be replaced during the next two to three days. Although the red blood cell count will take about two weeks to return to normal.

Donors are advised to leave about four clear days between donating and diving; during that time drink plenty of non-alcoholic fluids. Also leave four days between diving and donating.

Eating after diving

We know that the cardiovascular system is dynamic, see page 3-7, and altering blood flow (perfusion) may affect the outcome of a dive. Eating causes blood to be diverted (shunted) to the stomach to deal with the intake of new energy, which means there is less blood to remove excess nitrogen. Therefore, the decompression process may be compromised. It would be helpful to avoid eating large meals for at least two hours after stage-stop diving.

Medication (drugs)

There are, in general, two forms of medication: prescription and over-the-counter (OTC) medication.

It is wise to confirm with the doctor that your prescription medication is safe to dive with.

Always checkout, with a diving doctor, that your medication is safe to dive with.

A number of divers use OTC medication to help them breathe and overcome seasickness. The main question is not "Is it dangerous to dive whilst using drugs (medication)?" but "Am I well enough to dive?" Medication that clears airways may wear off during the dive, placing the diver at risk from reversed ear and damage to airways during the ascent.

Some medication alters blood flow and may influence the decompression protocol efficacy.

Medication, including anti-seasickness tablets, that causes drowsiness should be avoided.

Stress

Stress alters blood chemistry, which may affect your ability to tolerate stored excess nitrogen caused by diving. In the normal run of things this may be of little consequence. Dives on the limit, however, may be tipped over into a DCI situation. If possible avoid stress before diving, be relaxed and well rested.

Obesity

Early days of decompression research identified obesity as a factor in DCI. Much of this work centred on caisson workers who spent whole shifts under pressure. However, research by Wise (1963) and Curley (1989) found no association between DCI and body fat.

Recreational divers spend much less time under pressure so this phenomenon is not as relevant. Interestingly, body fat may even help protect against DCI in cold water.

The important question of defining obesity has recently been resolved: It's anyone fatter than the author.

PFO closure

The next question is: What to do about patent foramen ovales (PFOs)? Medical science tells us that between 20 and 25% of all people have a PFO. Since divers are a subset of the general population, the same follows. If this is true, it is worth noting that we are not seeing a 20 to 25% DCI incident rate. Furthermore, the medical profession is not proposing that all divers should be tested for PFOs. Those divers who are struck by DCI even a skin bend, following non-provocative diving should ask the question . . "Do I have a PFO?"

The good news is that PFOs can be repaired. Although this is a serious operation, it is not considered a major procedure and the patient can be back at work within about 40 hours of leaving hospital.

Keyhole surgery is used to access the heart via a blood vessel in the groin through which an endoscope and a special tool holding an "amplatzter occluder" (a PFO closer plug) are inserted and fed to the heart.

The amplatzter occluder, see Fig 6.24, is like a cuff link made of special inert wire {nickel and titanium (Nitinol)} that is compressed into a tiny tube for delivery. The wire mesh is filled with polyester fabric to help close the defect.

The leading flange of the device is passed through the PFO and opened, it is then pulled back against the septum of the heart and the trailing flange is released to form a captive porous plug. The delivery tool is now disconnected and removed. Over the next three months the endothelium (the membrane lining of the heart) will grow over the wire skeleton and close off the PFO.

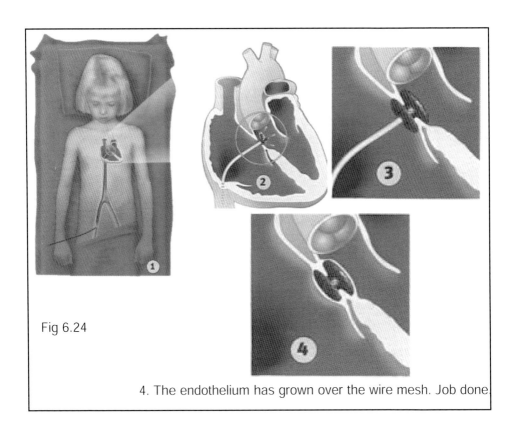

Fig 6.24

4. The endothelium has grown over the wire mesh. Job done.

Chapter 7
Multi-level PDC Assisted Diving

Nearer the limit

Multi-level PDC diving is very advanced diving, because it can bring a number of tissue compartments to their critical limit (M_0-value) at different times during the same dive and at the same time.

By design, traditional square profile techniques very often keep the sport diver from the full nitrogen burden permitted by the tables. This is because the system assumes that the full bottom time has been spent at the maximum depth of the dive. The very nature of sport diving is normally such that this is not the case. Usually only part of the dive time is spent at the maximum depth. Under these conditions the planned leading tissue compartment for the dive will not come under threat.

It is usually those who push the tables beyond their normal limits by intent or ignorance that suffer DCI; perhaps by staying that extra minute or so, or going a little deeper than intended and without proper modification of the decompression plan. They might ascend a little too fast, have one too many drinks in the pub the night before, or have not taken account of dehydration, obesity, medical/mental unfitness, increased age or old injuries, ie the behavioural factors!

Stage-stop diving equals cave diving!

The limits pushers include those who regularly practice "stage-stop" diving without due planning.

Many sport divers would not consider cave diving - because it is a bit too dodgy. . . . Stage-stop diving is rather like cave diving, once past the safety-stop limit the diver is denied free access to the surface, so that any out-of-air situation is potentially more serious than it might otherwise be. There is also increased danger in other situations where a prompt return to the surface is necessary.

Using a PDC during a multi-level dive means bottom times may be extended compared with traditional square-profile diving. For many divers this makes the need for stage-stop diving almost redundant. That's not to say that given sound reasons, proper planning and satisfactory sea and weather conditions stage-stop diving should be ruled out.

Leading tissue compartments

There are differences between M-LCAD and table diving. When using traditional tables the normal practice is to terminate the dive at - or nearly at - the M_0-value of the leading tissue. This means that one tissue controls the dive.

With PDC diving, nitrogen loadings are generally pushed further than in square-profile diving. This may mean that a number of tissue compartments approach their M_0-value. As the dive progresses, hopefully from the deeper to a shallower depth, the leading tissue may change from a fast to a slower compartment. This is why it is important to take a great deal of care when choosing and using a PDC. A wide spectrum of tissue compartments with moderate M and M_0-values offer a more protective solution.

Air/gas planning

M-LCAD techniques make the calculation of air/gas requirements more complicated and tedious, and are often omitted from the dive planning process. This will be discussed later in chapter 8, where a simplified alternative simplified method will be offered as a solution.

Saw-tooth dive profiles

PDC divers experience an almost unfettered freedom of movement underwater. This is clearly what we all want. However there is, sorry to say, a drawback and it is called the "saw-tooth dive profile". This is the practice of changing depth during the dive, eg to rise and fall.

If you cast your mind back to the topic of micro-bubbles you will recall that an ascent to the surface usually generates micro-bubbles (MBs).

For several reasons, including best bottom time value for your money as well as avoiding MBs, it is best to go directly to the maximum depth of the dive and then work steadily back to the surface. This should be at a rate of no more than 33ft/10m per minute, avoiding saw-tooth type profiles altogether.

In an ideal world every diver would follow the ideal dive-profile. Life is less than ideal and it's not always possible to avoid the saw-tooth profile. Where saw-tooth can't be avoided (ie wreck/reef diving etc), things should be taken very slowly. The rise parts of the profile should be slower than the 33ft/10m per minute, perhaps 16ft/5m per minute would be better.

Yo-yo dive profiles

A yo-yo dive profile is one where the diver surfaces part-way through a dive. This may be to find a lost partner, collect a forgotten piece of equipment or while training other divers.

Remember - a rise of as little as 13ft/4m can cause MBs. This fact is of special importance to the instructor during training sessions, for whom a better choice of gas would be Nitrox, see chapter 9.

It's also of particular importance that instructors limit the number of dives during a twenty-four hour period to the absolute minimum. This reduces the risk of damage that may be caused by a slow build-up of minute problems (bubble damage) as a result of many surfacings. Each surfacing should be treated as the end of a dive and be accompanied by a safety-stop. Slow ascents and safety-stops are of great importance under these conditions, see the sections on the oxygen window section and the intrapulmonary right-to-left shunts in chapter 3.

In the past it was thought that if the bottom time of a yo-yo type dive did not exceed the safety-stop time for the diving depth then all would be well. This is now in great doubt because of the MBs that may be generated and cause intrapulmonary right-to-left shunts and/or AGE.

Some people with many years of diving experience may feel that since they have not suffered problems that these ideas are just so much eye wash. A slow build-up of damage may not show itself for a number of years, and then it may be too late!

Dive depth sequence (forward/reverse dive profiles)

Care should be taken in the depth sequence of dives, see pages 2-14 and 6-12. Traditionally the best plan is to do the deepest dive of the day first, and then to work the other dives progressively shallower as the day goes on. The reasons are that:

- it provides the best value for your money in terms of bottom time
- if the dives are undertaken in any other order then it is more likely that slower tissue compartments will approach their M_0-values
- MBs may be forced though the lung filter to the arterial side of the circulation.

Correct stop depth

To obtain efficient decompression, it is important to make your stops as close as possible to the indicated ceiling shown on the PDC screen. Shallower will violate the procedure with the risk of DCI. Deeper will prolong the hang time, ie a 3 metre 10 minute stop taken at 6 metres could increase to 20 minutes or more. However, in the real world, rough surface conditions may force you into this situation. The comforting thought is that your PDC will adjust its calculations to cope. Be sure you have sufficient air for the job. For those using tables it is even more important to decompress at the tabulated depths because, unlike PDCs, tables cannot automatically adjust for excessive stop depths. Stop depths in excess of tabulated values can leave you seriously under-decompressed. This will make you vulnerable to DCI from the current dive, subsequent repetitive dives and/or flying etc.

Multi-level versus square profile diving

Many diving experts in the early days of PDC diving believed that PDCs would not be able to deal satisfactorily with the calculations of multi-level diving. However, there has been no mass increase in the DCI incident rate. But don't let that fool you into a false sense of security.

For the purposes of dive planning, divers were taught traditionally to assume that the whole dive takes place at the deepest depth recorded during the dive. This has a number of advantages:

- it is by far the simplest method in terms of both decompression and air planning
- only one tissue approaches its M_0-value at a time and
- if the whole dive is not at the maximum depth then no tissue comes under threat

This adds up to safe diving! Provided the behavioural factors are taken into account. However, this does have a limiting effect on bottom times.

It's clear that during the planning process, many dives are treated as square profile but are in practice multi-level.

Common sense tells us that 15 minutes spent at 30 metres will load the diver's body with more nitrogen than three minutes at 30 metres followed by 12 minutes at 24 metres.

Square dive profile v multi-level dive profile

Fig 7.1

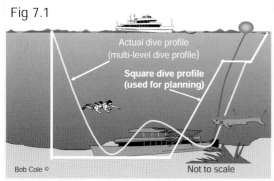

Actual dive profile
(multi-level dive profile)

**Square dive profile
(used for planning)**

Bob Cole ©   Not to scale

Using PDCs and multi-level diving techniques does, to some extent, take account of these differing depths and allows more time underwater. However, tables can offer a means of multi-level dive and air planning when used in conjunction with PDCs, see chapter 8.

Despite the cleverness of PDC devices the "chaos" factor still prevails - your best defence is proper and full planning, before you enter the water!

The reliability of modern PDCs is remarkable. Even so, it is wise, as with other kit, to prepare for equipment failure. A simple solution is to wear two PDCs.

This option is not as expensive as it might seem at first sight, when you consider that diving with a single PDC needs to be backed up with a submersible watch, depth gauge and a backup decompression plan.

Normally if a PDC fails, diving should be suspended for at least 24 hours. However, a back-up PDC allows you to continue diving. Another way of viewing the extra cost is to measure it against potential losses: a *basic* PDC costs no more than the over-all daily cost of "blue-water" diving (eg in the Red Sea) and it will help you avoid the above mentioned 24 hour diving abstention.

Preferably, the second or backup PDC should be of the same make, but perhaps with less bells and whistles.

Upgrading your PDC?

When considering a PDC up-grade, divers often talk about selling the old PDC on to defray the cost of the new one. Others bin the old one. Why? If it is still in working order and you can still get the batteries, why not hang on to it and clip it to your BCD as a back-up?

Chapter 8
Dive planning (gas)

Introduction

Good dive planning is essential to survival and it is helpful to remember the seven "Ps" - proper planning and preparation prevents piss poor performance. Dive planning can encompass a wide range of topics including:

- your current state of health and fitness to dive
- have you or your buddy the necessary experience for the proposed dive?
- the type of dive: training, wreck, drift, night, search etc
- visibility
- maximum depth, duration and gas requirements
- tides/current
- weather conditions
- equipment required
- communications - radio/mobile telephone, public phones
- emergency services
- permission to enter and dive the proposed site
- the dive leader and on-site conditions

However, from the annual incident statistics it seems fashionable to run out of air. Apart from being embarrassing it can force an ill-timed exit to the surface and lead to DCI. For this reason a section on air/gas planning is included, which I hope is of some help.

Gas requirements

All dives require an adequate supply of breathing gas and the wise diver will provide a contingency plan for the unforeseen and emergency purposes. But what does adequate mean and how do you figure out how much you need?

The body requires a certain amount of oxygen just for the

process of living. More oxygen will be required by a person who is working compared to a person at rest. So, clearly there is a relationship between oxygen consumption and the rate of work (or effort being exerted).

There are other aspects such as temperature, physical fitness and size. A cold, unfit, large person would use more oxygen than a warm, fit, small person. Divers need to consider factors such as: mental state, eg stress/anxiety. Is the diver calm or in a state of panic? How experienced is the diver?

An experienced diver is likely to require less oxygen than an inexperienced diver. These concepts are all very well, but how can they be related to the diver's need for gas and a method for determining the quantity required for a specific dive?

On the face of it, it would seem difficult. If we want to be scientific about it, it is very difficult indeed. However, a few basic rules have been developed that make the task quite simple. For example, at rest (watching television or reading a book) it is known that people consume between 0.3 and 0.5 litres of oxygen a minute, which means we breathe between 7.5 to 12.5 litres of air a minute. When walking, the breathing rate will likely double and running at a moderate pace could increase the rate to four times the resting value. Divers use a variety of gas mixtures: air, modified air or Nitrox, Trimix which contains oxygen, nitrogen and helium and a few use heliox which is a mix of oxygen and helium. So, for the purposes of this section "gas" will be used as a generic term to cover all breathing mixtures.

During most sport dives the work rate of the individual will vary: sometimes the diver will be at rest watching fish, perhaps taking a photograph, and at other times swimming from one place to another. So, trying to estimate gas consumption related to activity is difficult. However, for general purpose open circuit scuba diving, an average of 25 litres per minute is often used.

Furthermore, depth also increases the volume of gas consumed by the scuba diver. From earlier chapters you will know that the ambient pressure increases by one bar for every 10 metres of depth of sea water. This means that your gas consumption increases in line with the absolute pressure. At a depth of 10 metres, for the same effort, your gas consumption will be twice what it was on the surface and at 30 metres, you will use four times as much gas, because the pressure is four times the surface value.

Example:

If you breathe 25 litres of gas per minute on the surface (at 1 bar) and you intend to dive to say 20 metres, your gas requirements per minute for the dive, at 25 litres per minute per bar, would be :

25 litres/minute x 3 bar (absolute pressure) =

75 litres/minute

Fig 8.1 provides a table for various breathing rates:

Fig 8.1
A table of gas requirements in litres per minute

Gas Usage (l/min) @ surface	Litres/minute at depth (m)					
	10m	20m	30m	40m	50m	60m
15	30	45	60	75	90	105
20	40	60	80	100	120	140
25	50	75	100	125	150	175
30	60	90	120	150	180	210

© Bob Cole

To determine the gas requirement for a particular dive requires gas consumption (l/minute) and the time period of the dive in minutes. The general formula is as follows:

General formula for open circuit Scuba:

Surface gas consumption rate (l/min) x absolute pressure (bar)

=

Gas consumption at depth (Litres/minute)

l/min $_{Surface}$ x ({Depth ÷ 10} +1) = Gas consumption $_{depth}$ (Litres/minute)

From the above formula it is now possible to find the volume of gas required for a particular bottom time, say for example 30 minutes at 30 metres:

80 litres/minute x 30 minutes (BT) = **2400 litres**

What size diving cylinder?

A range of different sized dive cylinders

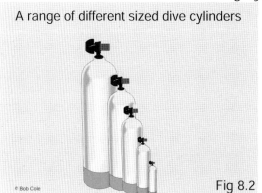

Fig 8.2

A visit to any dive shop will show that there are a variety of dive cylinders available with, at first sight, a bewildering range of sizes, see Fig 8.2. and Fig 8.3.

Each dive cylinder has a fixed maximum capacity of gas. The size is controlled by a number of fixed parameters.

Each cylinder has a working pressure (WP) which is given as a gauge pressure in bar. They also have a fixed volume when empty. This volume is measured by the amount of fresh water the cylinder can hold, measured in litres. This value is called the water capacity (WC).

Free-gas for a selection of dive cylinders

Water capacity (litres)	Working pressure (bar)	Free-gas capacity (litres)
10.0	204	2040
10.4	232	2412
12.0	204	2448
12.0	232	2784
15.0	232	3480

© Bob Cole

Fig 8.3

To find the free-gas or usable capacity of any cylinder is a simple matter of multiplying the water capacity (WC) in litres by the working pressure (WP) in bar.

Example: A diving cylinder with a water capacity (WC) of 10 litres and a working pressure (WP) of 232 bar has a free-gas capacity of: 10 litres x 232 bar = **2320 litres** *at sea level.* For safe diving it is essential to estimate your gas requirements for the proposed dive and to match your dive cylinder and its contents to your estimate.

The dive cylinder information such as water capacity (WC) in litres, working pressure (WP) in bar and test pressure (TP) also in bar are stamped on the top of the cylinder itself

Dive Cylinder Markings

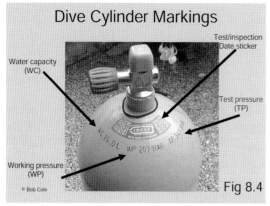

Water capacity (WC)

Test/inspection Date sticker

Test pressure (TP)

Working pressure (WP)

© Bob Cole

Fig 8.4

just below the neck, see Fig 8.4. Some cylinders may have their pressures in pounds per square inch (PSI). To convert PSI to bar divide by 14.51.

Confirm your gas consumption

The rate of 25 litres/minute/bar mentioned above is a general value and often used as the norm. However, individuals vary in their gas consumption, so it is good practice to measure your own consumption rates for differing activities ie low effort for *Photography, Exploration and Fish watching* (PEFing), and working hard such as finning against a current or using tools etc.

Respiratory minute volume (RMV)

Your respiratory minute volume (RMV) is a measure of how much gas you breathe under certain conditions for a given time - one minute. All divers should make an assessment of their own RMV, the method is given in chapter 6.

How much gas do we need?

The usual practice is match the gas requirements to the prepared decompression plan. A certain quantity of gas is then added to the calculated value for unforeseen events. The next step is to check that the dive cylinder holds sufficient gas for the dive.

Imagine a dive

You intend to do a non-working reef dive to a maximum depth of 24 metres for the maximum safety-stop bottom time. From the Bühlmann tables it can be seen that the bottom time must not exceed 25 minutes. The ascent rate is a maximum of 10 metres/minute and a one minute safety-stop is required at three metres. The dive cylinder has a water capacity (WC) of 12 litres and a maximum working pressure (WP) of 232 bar. For the purposes of gas planning assume a gas consumption rate of 25 litres/minute/bar.

i. Dive Gas - requirement for the dive bottom time

Absolute pressure = (Depth ÷ 10) + 1. So, at 24 metres

$$= (24/10) + 1 = 3.4 \text{ bar}$$

25 litres/minute/bar x 3.4 bar absolute pressure x 25 minutes bottom time = **2125 litres**

Note: The descent time is always assumed to be included in the bottom time.

This gives the gas required for the actual dive but ignores the ascent and safety-stop. For the purpose of gas planning ascents and safety-stops are treated as separate parts of the dive with their own gas requirements. Once calculated these are added to the gas required for the dive to produce a total gas requirement.

ii. Gas requirement for the ascent

There are a number of methods, but only two of the simple ones will be discussed here.

The ascent calculation is best kept simple. To do this the ascent is treated as a mini-dive at half the maximum depth for the total ascent time. This will give an average of the gas consumed during the whole ascent phase.

Maximum depth = 24 metres, half depth = 12 metres

Absolute pressure at 12 metres = (12 m/10) + 1 = 2.2 bar

Ascent time =

depth/ascent rate = 24m ÷ 10 = 2.4 minutes, say 3 minutes

Absolute pressure 2.2 bar x ascent time 3 minutes x 25 litres/minute = **165 litres**

iii. Gas requirement for the safety-stop

The safety-stop is at three metres and planned for one minute:

Absolute pressure at 3 metres = (3/10) + 1 = 1.3 bar

Gas requirement for the one minute safety-stop =

Absolute pressure 1.3bar x stop time 1 minute x 25 litres/minute = 32.5 litres, Say **33 litres**.

iv. Gas requirement for the dive

The gas requirement is the total of:

item i. Dive gas + *item ii.* Ascent gas requirement + *item iii.* Safety-stop gas =

$$2125 + 165 + 33 = \textbf{2323 litres}$$

Do you have sufficient gas in your 232 bar 12 litre dive cylinder?

The dive cylinder holds 232 bar x 12 litres = 2784 litres of gas. Clearly, since you require only 2323 litres for the dive, ascent and safety-stop, it is possible to complete the dive - provided there are no other complications! However, life is rarely that simple, so it is a wise person who includes a contingency for the unforeseen and for emergencies.

An alternative to this, which requires less calculation and is more conservative, is to add the ascent and stop time to the bottom time and calculate your total needs at the greatest depth. This system works well for standard one minute safety-stop dives or where stage-stops times are minimal. This can, however, be excessively restrictive for longer stage-stops dives.

Back-up or emergency gas

There is no substitute for accurate dive planning and this means thinking through the whole dive, visualising all eventualities including safety/stage-stops, work load, tide/current, water temperature, admitting to your own physical fitness limitations etc etc. After all this planning there is the need to provide a reserve of gas - but how much and how is it to be provided? Remember, you are providing not just for your own unexpected breathing rate, but also for your buddy's potential out-of-gas (OoG) problem. It is also worth noting that due to the stress of an OoG situation, buddy teams have been known to breathe up to five times their normal rate.

There is a fixed mechanical reserve system called the J-valve. This dive cylinder valve restricts the gas flow to the diver when the pressure drops to a predetermined value - about 50 bar. To gain access to the reserve gas the diver must pull a lever attached to the J-valve.

This system has severe limitations and it is recommended that you calculate your own reserve.

But how much should the reserve value be? Many contents pressure gauges have a red area on the face indicating 0-50 bar cylinder pressure.

Clearly a 50 bar reserve is better than a 30 bar. But will 50 bar be sufficient? Well, it will depend upon the type of diving being undertaken. Cave divers use the so-called "rule-of-thirds". They use one third for the outward swim, one third for the home swim and one third as reserve. Clearly this is the best option so far. However cave divers, and for that matter wreck divers who penetrate wrecks, carry additional independent gas supply(s): either a pony cylinder, a twin set or side mount cylinder(s). The combinations of dive cylinder arrangements are extensive. For the sport diver, is there the need for a massive backup? The rule should be: kit up for the situation. Cave diving needs a great deal more backup than reef diving. In general, multiply your total gas requirement by:

· 1.33 for safety-stop diving

· 1.5 for stage-stop diving and wreck penetration diving

This level of back-up gas should also be able to support the gas compensation required for your BCD and/or dry suit.

All instructors should carry an independent gas supply. Indeed, it would be wise for all divers to carry an independent supply.

Returning to the earlier dive plan, you can now calculate the required reserve gas for the dive: the bottom time gas supply was calculated to be 2323 litres.

· Assuming this is a safety-stop dive, then this should be multiplied by 1.33 to find the total requirement:

2323 x 1.33 = 3089.5 litres, say **3090 litres**

· Assuming this is a wreck penetration dive, then this should be multiplied by 1.5 to find the total requirement:

2323 x 1.5 = 3384.5 litres, say **3485 litres**

In each case, this ensures that a reasonable gas supply will be available for unforeseen or emergency purposes. In this exercise the dive cylinder has been pumped to 232 bar and only provides 2784 litres of free-gas. In both cases, there is insufficient gas for the plan. There are two simple solutions. Cut the bottom time back to meet the available gas, including the reserve gas. Or, use a larger cylinder or multiple cylinders.

An alternative method - Gas tables in bar / minute at depth

The above calculations are not difficult, but they are tedious and not best done on board a moving boat. Furthermore, free-gas calculations give requirements in litres which need conversion to gauge reading.

A better way is to prepare your own simple-to-use gas table for use in the field which can show your gas needs as a pressure gauge reading in bar.

These tables are simple to construct using the methods already discussed. Calculate the gas requirements, as shown earlier, for one minute at three metres, six metres and for each of the depths shown on your decompression tables. Divide each value by the water capacity of the cylinder to be used. Now all you have to do is multiply each depth by bottom times that are to your liking eg 5, 10, 15 and 20 minutes as shown in Fig 8.5.

A sample gas planning table for a 12litre dive cylinder

Fig 8.5	Bottom/Actual Bottom Time (Minutes)				
	1	5	10	15	20
Depth (m)	Gauge pressure (bar)				
3	2.7	14	27	41	54
6	3.4	17	34	50	68
9	4.0	20	40	60	80
12	4.6	23	46	69	92
15	5.2	26	52	78	104
18	5.9	30	59	89	118
21	6.5	33	65	98	130
24	7.1	36	71	107	142
27	7.7	39	77	116	154
30	8.4	42	84	126	168

© Bob Cole

Note: *These gas tables are dive cylinder water capacity (WC) specific, but not confined to a given working pressure (WP).*

Using this table to determine the gas needs for the earlier worked example of a safety-stop dive to 24 metres for a bottom time of 25 minutes:

i. Bottom time gas in bar

Gauge reading for a 25 minute bottom time can be obtained by either multiplying the one minute gauge reading by 25 or adding the 5 and 20 minute values together:

$$25 \times °7.1 = 177.5 \text{ bar, say 178 bar or}$$

$$°36 + *142 = 178 \text{ bar}^1$$

ii. Ascent gas in bar

The rise time from 24 metres is 2.4 minutes, say 3 minutes at half the dive depth, ie 12 metres:

$$\text{The ascent gas} = 3 \times °4.6 = 13.8 \text{ say 14 bar}^2$$

iii. Safety-stop gauge reading

The safety-stop is one minute at three metres:

$$1 \times °2.7 = 2.7, \text{ say 3 bar}^3$$

iv. Dive gas in bar

The previous method (p8-7) found a requirement of 2323 litres, which is equal to a cylinder pressure of 193.58 bar, say 194 bar. Almost identical when the rounding-up is taken into account.

Total gauge pressure reading required for this dive is the above items added together:

$$178 \text{ bar}^1 + 14 \text{ bar}^2 + 3 \text{ bar}^3 = 195 \text{ bar}$$

Clearly this pressure gauge reading is very close to the earlier calculations and when multiplied by 1.33 or 1.5 to account for the reserve will exceed the cylinders 232 bar working pressure. As with the previous method this can be overcome by either cutting the bottom time back to meet the available gas, including the reserve gas. Or, by using a larger cylinder or multiple cylinders.

Chapter 9
An introduction to some alternative decompression systems

Introduction

Nature didn't say air is for divers. It's not the best mixture of gases for diving. It has a number of properties that limit its functionality: nitrogen narcosis, oxygen toxicity and a heavy decompression obligation:

1   Nitrogen narcosis: a form of drunkenness (or diver dysfunction), starts in a mild form as shallow as 30 metres and gets progressively worse with depth.

2   Oxygen is required to support life, however, as in other situations, too much of a good thing may become unhelpful. At a depth of about 66 metres air is knocking on the door of toxicity when the pO_2 reaches 1.6 bar. Oxygen toxicity itself won't kill you, but if you blackout underwater you could drown.

3   Compared to some other gas mixtures air carries an excessive decompression obligation.

Modifying the diver's breathing gas has benefits. This is not a new idea: the British were using Nitrox (oxygen enriched air) in the early part of the 20th century and the US Navy were playing with oxygen/helium mixtures during the 1930s. Sport diving has expanded its horizons by adopting an appropriate gas mix for each dive, instead of just using air.

Nitrox

Nitrox is just a blend of oxygen and nitrogen that is different in proportion to the 21/79% of standard air. The full name given to Nitrox is Enriched Air Nitrox (EAN_x) and by convention referred to by the oxygen percentage. The "x" in EAN_x is the oxygen content say 32% and is written EAN_{32}. The balance of gas in this mix, is of course 68% nitrogen.

The benefits come from the fact that less nitrogen at any given depth will produce a smaller decompression burden than air for the same dive. Furthermore, the reduction in nitrogen also reduces the effects of nitrogen narcosis.

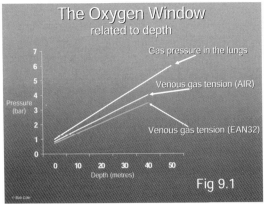

The Oxygen Window
related to depth

Gas pressure in the lungs

Venous gas tension (AIR)

Venous gas tension (EAN32)

Pressure (bar)

Depth (metres)

Fig 9.1

The down side is that the increased proportion of oxygen brings oxygen toxicity closer to the surface compared to air. This makes the gas suitable for shallow water diving in the range down to 40 metres. Great for recreational diving.

The reduction of decompression obligation is accompanied with a widening of the oxygen window, which if used wisely will improve safety during the ascent phase of a dive. This widening of the oxygen window is compared to air in Fig 9.1. It is important to note that as with air the oxygen window narrows as the diver nears the surface, at which time extra care is needed in controlling the ascent rate.

Some standard EAN_x mixtures
with recommended pO_2 and max depths

EAN_x % mix	Recommended pO_2 (bar)	Maximum depth (m)
21	1.4	50
28	1.4	40
32	1.4	33
36	1.4	28
40	1.4	25

© Bob Cole

Fig 9.2

Since there is a danger of oxygen toxicity, training agencies have placed safety restrictions on the maximum pO_2 attained during a dive. Typically, the recommended maximum pO_2 is set at 1.4 bar. In the UK there are five standard mixtures, including air, to choose from, see Fig 9.2.

The standard method for calculating the decompression obligation is to use the Equivalent Air Depth (EAD) technique. This involves the use of the following formula to determine nitrogen

$$EAD = \{(1 - FO_2) \times (D + 10) \div 0.79\} - 10$$

Where:

FO_2 = the per unit fraction of oxygen in the breathing mix, eg 0.36 is used for 36%.

D = depth in metres.

As an example: If a diver made a dive to say 28 metres using EAN_{36} what would be the equivalent air depth?

$$EAD = \{(1-.036) \times (28 + 10) \div 0.79\} -10$$

$$= 20.78 \text{ metres say } \textbf{21 metres}$$

Using the Bühlmann decompression tables the diver would plan the dive at 21 metres instead of 28 metres. A 28 metre dive is treated as if it were at 30 metres and the safety-stop bottom time would be 17 minutes, whereas using EAN_{36} and 21 metres the safety-stop bottom time becomes 35 minutes, an increase of 105%!

A look-up Table of EANx mixes, Depths and EADs

EANx gas mixes, Depths and EADs			
EAN28 Depth/EAD	EAN32 Depth/EAD	EAN36 Depth/EAD	EAN40 Depth/EAD
10/9m	12/9m	13/9m	15/9m
14/12m	15/12m	17/12m	19/12m
17/15m	19/15m	21/15m	23/15m
20/18m	22/18m	24/18m	_25/18m_
24/21m	26/21m	_28/21m_	**27/18m**
27/24m	29/24m	**31/24m**	**_30/21m_**
30/27m	_33/27m_	**34/27m**	
34/30m	**36/30m**		
37/33m	**_40/33m_**		
_40/36m_		As issued to the Sub-Aqua Association (GB) by The Dive Information Company © Bob Cole	
43/39m			
_47/42m_			

© Bob Cole

Fig 9.3

Note: In the above table:

i. The EADs underlined are at a pO_2 of 1.4 bar.

ii. The EADs in **Bold** are at about a pO_2 of 1.48 bar.

iii. Those EADs in **Bold underlined Italics** are approaching or at 1.6 bar.

For standard mixtures there is a set of look-up tables that allows the EAD to be determined without the need for the above mentioned calculation, see Fig 9.3. This is used in conjunction with the decompression tables.

Alternatively, you could use a Nitrox PDC or a custom software package to "cut" a specific solution for the dive at hand. One training agency offers a Nitrox decompression table system that does not use the EAD approach. This involves seven tables for each breathing gas mixture.

In Nitrox diving it is necessary to track not only the decompression obligation but also the uptake and elimination of oxygen. This is to avoid pulmonary damage from long exposures to high levels of oxygen and the much faster and potentially fatal effects on the central nervous system (CNS) from high pressure oxygen. Although this is relatively simple to manage it is outside the scope of this decompression book and the reader is directed to seek specialist training in this field of operation.

Other breathing mixtures

Safe decompression is only one of the factors that a diver has to think about. Another important factor is nitrogen narcosis (N_2N) which starts to have an effect at about 30m/100ft. Narcosis is likened to drunkenness that increases with depth and has been christened, by some, the

"Martini Effect" and is equal to drinking one Martini on an empty stomach, every 15 metres.

Well, they like to think so!

Clearly people differ in their susceptibility to alcohol and the same is true of N_2N. Furthermore, hardened drinkers like experienced divers can withstand the effects of their respective delights better than the novice. The effects are also moderated by such things as: a slow rate of descent, temperature (warm water), and visual stimulus (good viz). Even so the problem does not go away! Using air down to 50 metres produces an acceptable degree of N_2N; this can be eased by the use of Nitrox down to 40 metres. Nonetheless, beyond 50 metres N_2N becomes progressively more difficult to deal with.

Risk assessment tells us that we should assess all situations and try to eliminate potential hazards or at least reduce their potential for harm.

Relative Narcotic Potential

Inert gas	Narcotic potential	Solubility in lipid	Least narcotic
Helium (H_e)	4.26	0.015	
Neon (N_e)	3.8	0.019	
Hydrogen (H_2)	1.83	0.036	
Nitrogen (N_2)	1.00	0.067	
Argon (A)	0.43	0.14	
Krypton (K_r)	0.14	0.43	Most narcotic

© Bob Cole

Fig 9.4

It has been discovered that replacing the nitrogen in the breathing mixture with another inert gas alters the narcotic effect. It would seem that the solubility of a gas in lipid is a measure of its narcotic effect, see Fig 9.4. The "Relative Narcotic Potency" of each gas is compared with nitrogen which is taken as unity or 1. It can be seen that helium (He) is 4.26 times less narcotic than nitrogen. Neon (Ne) looks a good candidate at 3.58 times less than N_2. However, its molcular weight is five times that of He but only about two thirds of N_2. This makes Ne easier breathe than air at depth, but not as easy as He.

which makes it more difficult to breathe at greater depth. The problems increase further, when the costs implications and the lack of a commercially available set of decompression tables or software package are added into the equation.

A plentiful alternative with good breathing characteristics is hydrogen (H_2); however, it becomes explosive when the oxygen content of the breathing mix exceeds 4%. All other gases have worse narcotic characteristics than nitrogen.

The down side to helium is that it dissipates body heat very fast. In the professional world of diving this is overcome by the use of water-heated suits, whereas sport divers with relatively short exposures (dive times) fill their dry suits with argon (A) which is a better insulator than air. This topic is outside the scope of this book and the reader is directed to take a suitable course on advanced/technical diving techniques.

So then, helium is the make-weight gas of choice for the professional and for the sport diver. But a different decompression system is required because the uptake and elimination of helium, provided there are no micro-bubbles, is 2.65 times faster than nitrogen. For helium based dives, decompression stops start deeper than for an equivalent air dive. This is to cope with the rapid off-gassing and possible bubbling that is caused by the speed of the gas exchange.

Heliox

Heliox - a blend of helium and oxygen. Heliox provides the option for avoiding narcosis altogether. However, there is rarely a single all-singing all-dancing solution to any problem and this is no exception. Excluding the problems of body heat loss, helium has another difficulty that becomes apparent at 152m/500ft and beyond - high-pressure nervous syndrome (HPNS), which causes a decrement in motor and intellectual performance that is accompanied by dizziness, nausea, vomiting and a marked tremor of hands, arms and torso. This problem is suppressed by a slow pressurisation (descent) and the inclusion of a small amount of nitrogen in the breathing mixture. The "Technical Diver" training agencies warn that HPNS may start at or about 120m/394ft (ie at about P_{ab} 13 bar).

This topic is outside the range of sport diving and the scope of this book. For more information, the reader is directed to read "The Physiology and Medicine of Diving" by Bennett and Elliott.

Now that nitrogen narcosis (N_2N) is eliminated and ignoring the other factors mentioned above there are still other issues to deal with: oxygen toxicity and decompression.

The threat of oxygen toxicity is related to the pO_2 of the gas mixture being inhaled. If the ratio of oxygen to helium is maintained at the same proportions as air (ie 21%), then the outer limit of pO_2 1.6 bar (used by some training agencies) will be attained at:

$$\{(1.6 \div 0.21) - 1\} \times 10 = \textbf{66.19 metres}$$

So under these conditions the air depth limit would apply.

Without the N_2N burden the pO_2 at the planned operating depth can be adjusted, within limits, to the diver's needs.

You will know that human life can be supported on the surface by a pO_2 of 0.21 bar. Given that this is also true underwater, the breathing mix can be adjusted to match the diver's needs during the dive. Here is the next compromise; the nearer the pO_2 is adjusted to the surface value of 0.21 bar, the greater the decompression burden for any given dive. Between 0.21 and 0.5 bar there is no need to worry about oxygen absorption and oxygen toxicity. Beyond 0.5 bar of oxygen it must be tracked to ensure the safe limits are not violated.

Life is full of compromises or trade-offs. Within the relatively short bottom time encountered in sport diving (technical diving) compared to professional saturation diving, it is reasonable to elevate the pO_2 up to say 1.4 bar. This allows a single oxygen exposure of 150 minutes.

On a dive to say 80 metres with a pO_2 of 1.4 bar the breathing mixture would be calculated as follows:

the ambient pressure at 80 metres =

$$(80 \div 10) + 1 = 9 \text{ bar}$$

the percentage of helium required in the mix at this depth is:

$$\{(9 - 1.4) \div 9\} \times 100 = 84.44\%$$

and the oxygen content would be:

$$100 - 84.44 = 15.56\%$$

The concept of gas switching

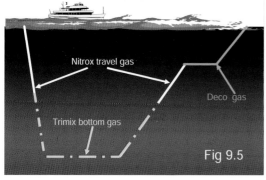

Nitrox travel gas

Deco gas

Trimix bottom gas

Fig 9.5

Clearly, at the surface a pO_2 of 0.1556 bar would be below that which could safely support human life.

To overcome this problem, a travel mix is required to take the diver from the surface to a depth where the bottom mix would be safe to use. In this case, the bottom gas reaches a pO_2 of 0.21 bar at a depth of 3.59 metres. In practice, however, divers use a Nitrox mix as a travel gas and descend to a depth that creates a pO_2 of 1.4 bar and then change to the bottom gas. During the ascent the bottom gas is used to ascend to the depth limit of the travel gas, see Fig 9.5. This procedure also reduces the decompression burden created by the ascent/descent. This would also be followed by the use of a richer Nitrox mix(s) or pure oxygen at the stops to further reduce the decompression obligation. This is a simple example of the procedure of gas switching, there are many more and they can become very complex.

The nitrogen/helium decompression curves cross-over at about two hours, after which using heliox has an advantage in shorter decompression times. In the professional diving world the helium would be recovered and reused, so using heliox can be cost effective. Although other, non-decompression, factors also need to be taken into account.

For the sport diver the cost of helium and the waste of using it with open circuit scuba, heliox diving is very expensive and is normally outside the realms of sport diving. There are alternatives.

Heliair is Trimix. It is a cheap and easy way of mixing Trimix using helium and air instead of helium, O_2, air air. There is, however, a limitation on the achievable % range of each gas in the mix.

Trimix (and Heliair)

The compromise is Trimix, a combination of oxygen (O_2), nitrogen (N_2) and helium (He). With open circuit scuba it provides an relatively cheap alternative to heliox. As with any compromise the solution is far from perfect. Again, a special decompression system is required. One that can cope with two make-weight or so-called diluent gases.

The whole Trimix system is a balance or a compromise to achieve the required result. As with heliox diving, the diver needs to control the pO_2 within safe limits.

The next gas to get right is the nitrogen. With Trimix the diver can "dial" or determine a desired level of nitrogen narcosis (N_2N). This is called the "Equivalent Nitrogen (or Narcotic)" Depth or "END-depth".

Once the maximum operating depth has been determined the pO_2 can be set (as shown overleaf for heliox). The END-depth is set in a similar way, again using Dalton's Law of partial pressures.

Take a dive to say 60m where the P_{ab} is:

$$P_{ab} = 60 \div 10 + 1 = 7 \text{ bar}$$

Now assuming a pO_2 of say **1.33 bar** . . . (1)

and an END-depth of say 31 metres is required, the nitrogen pN_2 would be:

$$pN_2 = P_{ab} \times 0.79$$

$$= (31 \div 10) + 1 \times 0.79 = \textbf{3.24 bar} \ldots \qquad (2)$$

All that is now required is the pHe, which is found as follows:

$$pHe = P_{ab} - (pO_2 + pN_2)$$

$$= 7 - (1.33 + 3.24) = \textbf{2.43 bar} \ldots \qquad (3)$$

From this information the percentage of each gas in the breathing mixture can be determined.

Since the total pressure at 60 metres is 7 bar the percentage or fraction (FO_2) of oxygen is:

$$1.33 \div 7 \times 100 = 19\% \ldots \qquad (4)$$

and the nitrogen percentage or fraction (FN_2) is:

$$3.34 \div 7 \times 100 = 47.71\% \ldots \qquad (5)$$

Clearly the percentage or fraction (FHe) of helium is:

$$100 - (19 + 47.71) = 33.29\% \ldots \qquad (6)$$

As with Nitrox there is a convention for describing Trimix:

$$O_2/He/N_2 \text{ - and in this case: } 19/34/47$$

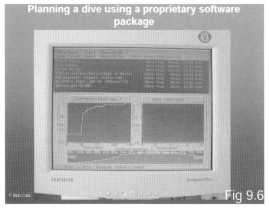

Planning a dive using a proprietary software package

Fig 9.6

It is a bit tedious to do these calculations for each dive and may be difficult to match with a decompression table. As usual a range of standard breathing mixtures that predetermined the maximum operating depth have been developed by the technical training agencies.

However, the general solution is to use a laptop computer with a decompression software program, see Fig 9.6. The program is relatively simple to operate; it asks for type of breathing mix (air, nitrox, trimix), the type of dive equipment (open circuit scuba, semi-closed rebreather or closed circuit rebreather). When a mix other than air is selected, the program asks for the percentage of each gas being used. Now the depth options are input (multiple depths can be selected), along with each bottom time. The software program then calculates the required decompression profile for the information that has been supplied.

Currently there are about six on the market with a range of complexity. Many are based upon Albert Bühlmann's algorithm, usually with bolted-on safety factors and bubbles models. It should be remembered that as with all decompression systems there are no guarantees.

The concept of "Run Time"

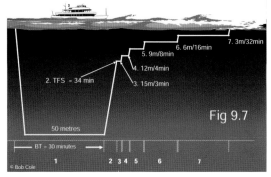

7. 3m/32min
6. 6m/16min
5. 9m/8min
4. 12m/4min
3. 15m/3min
2. TFS = 34 min

50 metres

BT = 30 minutes

1   2 3 4 5   6   7

Fig 9.7

Run Time Chart

Dive section	Depth (m)	Run time (min)
1. Bottom Time	50m	30 min
2. Time to 1st Stop	15m	34 min
3. Leave time	15m	37 min
4. Leave time	12m	41 min
5. Leave time	9m	49 min
6. Leave time	6m	65 min
7. Leave time	3m	98 min
	Total	99 min

Fig 9.8

Run Time system

It is usual to plan the dive using the "Run Time" system, where each section of the dive is planned to the nearest minute, see Figs 9.7 and 9.8, and gas changes must be precise otherwise the decompression plan is violated and DCI will take its vengeance! Back-up plans and escape routes are essential.

This system of diving requires proper training, a great deal of experience and religious discipline.

PDCs

An alternative to the above is available. At the time of going to press there were two PDCs available that can handle, amongst other systems and gases, Trimix. It is important to realise that even with a PDC as advanced as these two, things can still go toes-up. This means there is no avoiding the back-up plans and escape routes mentioned above.

Rebreathers

The panacea to all decompression ills and bottom times seems to be on offer with the use of a rebreather. Panacea? Nothing could be further from the truth!

Clearly, under certain circumstances rebreathers offer a solution, but nothing comes alone. Basically, there are two types; semi-closed circuit rebreather (SCR) and closed-circuit circuit rebreather (CCR). Each has its place, its benefits and its disadvantages.

Note: The arrows within the diagram denote the gas flow around the breathing loop.

Rebreathers are Scuba sets that re-circulate the diver's exhaled breath instead of discharging it into the water where it is wasted to the surface. This is a more efficient method of using breathing gas.

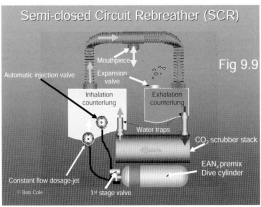

Semi-closed Circuit Rebreather (SCR)

Fig 9.9

Mouthpiece
Automatic injection valve
Expansion valve
Inhalation counterlung
Exhalation counterlung
Water traps
CO_2 scrubber stack
EAN, premix Dive cylinder
Constant flow dosage-jet
© Bob Cole
1st stage valve

Semi-closed Circuit Re-breather (SCR)

This chapter deals only with the decompression aspects of using a SCR. So the brief description that follows is exactly that - "brief".

The rebreather idea dates back many years before the Cousteau and Gagnan's aqualung. The SCR is a very basic piece of kit that simply takes the diver's exhaled breath and guides it around a semi-closed breathing loop into a canister that contains absorbent material (soda lime) to extract the diver's exhaled CO_2. The gas then moves around the loop into the inhalation breathing bag (counterlung) where additional breathing gas is added, see Fig 9.9. The inflow of breathing gas from the pre-mix dive cylinder via a dosage-jet is constant, irrespective of depth; so that if it is set at say 10 litres per minute a 4 litre 200 bar dive cylinder would last 80 minutes at the surface or at its working depth or anywhere in between. Whereas a 10 litre open circuit scuba cylinder used at say 25 metres at the same rate would be exhausted in just 67 minutes. More likely the breathing rate would be about 18 litres per minute exhausting the cylinder in just 37 minutes.

Because the inflow of gas is constant the system must be vented, hence the term "semi-closed", otherwise the flexible counterlungs would explode.

The system works on the basis that the breathing gas is supplied from a pre-mixed Nitrox cylinder. Initially the gas in the breathing bag (inhalation counterlung) is the same concentration as that in the dive cylinder. Once the dive is in motion the fraction of inhaled oxygen (FiO_2) is modified to a weaker mix by the diver breathing the circulating gas in the breathing loop.

The reduction in FiO_2 is due to the consumption of oxygen by the diver. The heavier the workload the more oxygen is consumed and the weaker the Nitrox mix in the inhalation counterlung. This affects the diver's decompression obligation.

For this reason it is necessary for the diver to estimate the workload of the dive, and therefore the oxygen consumption rate (VO_2). For sport diving a VO_2 of between one and two litres per minute is adopted. For an average non-working dive one litre of oxygen per minute is usual. Unlike air consumption, oxygen consumption is linked to the metabolic rate not depth. Therefore, provided the work-rate does not exceed the planned maximum, usage of oxygen consumed per minute will not alter from the surface to the deepest depth of the dive and back again.

As with open circuit Scuba Nitrox diving, the maximum depth of the dive is determined by the pO_2, normally 1.4 bar. In the SCR case, the fraction of inspired oxygen (FiO_2) in the inhalation counterlung is set by a combination of three things; the breathing mix, the dosage-jet (flow-rate) and the work-rate.

The standard formula to calculate the average fraction of oxygen (FiO_2) in the inhalation counterlung is as follows:

This system assumes that the breathing mix during the dive will be in a "steady state".

$$FiO_2 = \frac{\{Flow\text{-}rate\ (Q_s) \times Cylinder\ FO_2\} - VO_2}{(Flow\text{-}rate\ (Q_s) - VO_2)}$$

Where:

Flow-rate (Q_s) is the constant flow-rate of the dosage-jet.

The cylinder FO_2 is the pre-mix Nitrox in the dive cylinder, and VO_2 is the diver's oxygen consumption rate in litres/minute.

EANx mixes, Flow-rates (Q_{2min}), FiO_2 and Depths and EADs. Assuming a VO_2 of 1litre/min			
EAN32 Q_{Smin} = 15.5l/min FiO_2 = 0.27	EAN40 Q_{Smin} = 10.4l/min FiO_2 = 0.33	EAN50 Q_{Smin} = 7.3l/min FiO_2 = 0.42	EAN60 Q_{Smin} = 5.3l/min FiO_2 = 0.51
Depth/EAD	Depth/EAD	Depth/EAD	Depth/EAD
10/9m	12/9m	16/9m	12/3.7m
13/12m	16/12m	_18/10m_	_13/4.3m_
17/15m	19/15m	**20/12m**	**14/4.8m**
20/18m	23/18m	**_22/15m_**	**_16/6.1m_**
23/21m	_26/21m_		
27/24m	**_30/24m_**		
30/27m			
33/30m		By	
36/33m		The Dive Information Company	
_40/36m_		© Bob Cole	

© Bob Cole

Fig 9.10

Note, in the above table:

i. The EADs under-lined are at a pO_2 of 1.4 bar.

ii. The EADs in **Bold** are at about a pO_2 of 1.48 bar.

iii. Those EADs in **_Bold underlined Italics_** are approaching or at 1.6 bar.

Important: The pO_2 is calculated at the working depth, not the EAD, using the EANx of the supply cylinder, not the FiO_2 from the counterlung.

Example:

For a dive to say 17metres using EAN60 and a dosage-jet flow-rate of 5.7 litre/minute with no planned heavy work (so an oxygen consumption rate (VO_2) of 1 litre/minute will be used):

$$FiO_2 = \frac{(5.7 \times \{60 \div 100\}) - 1}{(5.7 - 1)}$$

$$FiO_2 = \mathbf{0.514}$$

use 0.5 or 50%

This information is used in the standard formula to find the EAD of the planned dive:

$$EAD = \frac{(1 - Fi_{O2}) \times (D + 10)}{0.79} - 10$$

$$\frac{(1 - 0.5) \times (17 + 10)}{0.79} - 10 = \textbf{7.08 metres}$$

For standard mixtures there is a set of look-up tables that allows the EAD to be determined without the need for the above mentioned calculation, see Fig 9.10. This is used in conjunction with the decompression tables.

Caution required

When the diver pre-estimates workload, it is not possible to determine the exact FiO_2 throughout the dive. For this reason it is essential to be cautious and not underestimate the oxygen consumption rate.

Using a PDC

If you want to use a standard Nitrox computer all that is required is to dial the calculated FiO_2 into the PDC and it will do the rest.

Note: The setpoint is a compromise which needs to be thought about. High setpoints reduce the decompression obligation but may increase the risk of oxygen toxicity. A low setpoint increases the decompression required but reduces the oxygen toxicity problems. This can only be dealt with on a proper training course.

For those with the appropriate amount of cash, there is a PDC that actually measures, in real time, the FiO_2 in the breathing loop and transmits that information, by radio, to the wrist-mounted PDC which uses the information in its workload related decompression calculations.

For more information about rebreather diving the reader is directed to "Rebreather Diving" ISBN 0 9519337 9 5.

Closed Circuit Rebreathers (CCR)

In a CCR the gas circulating within the closed circuit system is only vented during an ascent. In all other conditions the system is closed.

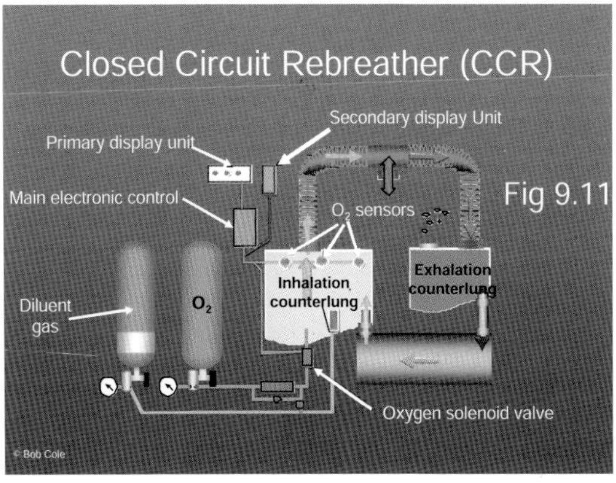

Closed Circuit Rebreather (CCR)

Secondary display Unit
Primary display unit
Main electronic control
O_2 sensors
Fig 9.11
Inhalation counterlung
Exhalation counterlung
Diluent gas
O_2
Oxygen solenoid valve
© Bob Cole

In a modern closed circuit rebreather system, the circulating gas control differs from an SCR in that the oxygen addition, from a pure oxygen dive cylinder, is initiated by the diver's metabolic rate (ie as the O_2 is consumed) and is managed by oxygen sensors, an electronic logic system and a solenoid valve.

Oxygen sensors may drift in their ability to give an accurate determination of the oxygen content in the breathing loop. For this reason three oxygen sensors are employed in conjunction with an electronic logic voting system that monitors the partial pressure of the oxygen in the inhalation section of the breathing loop, see Fig 9.11. The system is looking for differences between the sensors. Normally, if one sensor gives a drastically different reading from the other two it is assumed to be faulty, its reading is ignored by the processor, and the dive is terminated.

The objective of the system is to maintain a constant pO_2 throughout the dive. On the surface, at the outset of the dive the required pO_2 ('the so-called "setpoint") is determined and entered into the CCR's monitoring system. For sport diving this is normally set at 1.3 bar, which allows an oxygen exposure of up to three hours.

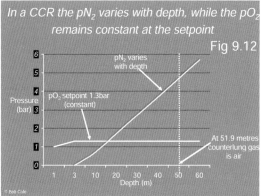

In a CCR the pN_2 varies with depth, while the pO_2 remains constant at the setpoint

Fig 9.12

The idea of a constant pO_2 throughout the dive is a major departure from all other diving and decompression systems, see Fig 9.12.

All other methods of diving and decompression use the idea that the gases in the breathing mixture are at a constant percentage.

From the graph in Fig 9.12 it can be seen for a dive to 30 metres, with a setpoint of 1.3 bar, that during the ascent the percentage of nitrogen inhaled is reducing with depth until at 1.3 metres the diver is breathing pure oxygen. This is automatic and makes for very efficient decompression.

Example: Fig 9.13 shows the reduction, to 1/3rd, in decompression time required for a 30 minute dive to 51 metres using a CCR with air as the diluent compared to the same dive using open circuit Scuba and air.

Stops required for 30 minutes at 51 metres
CCR v Open Circuit Air   Fig 9.13

Stop depth (m)	CCR deco time (min)	OC Scuba (air) deco time (min)
3	11	36
6	6	18
9	4	8
12	2	6
15	-	2
Total deco time	**23**	**70**
CNS%	37	16
UPTDs	100	49

© Bob Cole

This method of diving requires special constant pO_2 decompression tables, which are "cut" using special decompression software and a PC. Alternatively, a constant pO_2 PDC can be used.

On inspection of the graph in Fig 9.10 it can be seen that if the diluent is air, then despite a constant pO_2 of 1.3 bar the mix in the breathing loop becomes equal to air at a depth of about 52 metres. From this point on the EAD of the dive becomes greater than air as does the nitrogen narcosis. Even if the setpoint is increased to say 1.4 bar the depth limitation, using air as the diluent, is 56 metres.

To reduce the nitrogen narcosis the diluent gas needs to include helium (He).

Many divers use Trimix in their CCR. There is, however, a theoretical problem with this method, which comes about because the gas mixing system only monitors the oxygen content in the loop. This may leave a doubt as to the true mix within the breathing loop. Apart from oxygen measurement errors there are two other sources of error. A gas blending error and the circulating error caused by the fact that three gases of differing molecular weights are competing for access through the same entry jet.

An alternative is to use Heliox, which becomes cost viable because the system is closed and very little helium is used.

Important Notice

The decompression concepts discussed in this chapter are more than a step beyond the run of the mill resort/club diving and require special training.

If, having read this chapter, you may wish to extend your diving activities, I urge you to seek professional training from a suitable diver training agency.

Chapter 10
Risk assessment

Introduction

No matter how much diving is glamorised by television and glossy brochures, it remains a risk sport. There are no guarantees.

For some, risk is part of the excitement. For others, the thrill of being underwater with the wildlife is sufficient. Whatever your point of view, you have responsibilities to:

☑ other divers

☑ trainee divers

☑ other water users

☑ rescuers and the emergency services

☑ the general public

☑ your family, and

☑ yourself

We all have a duty placed on us to act with reasonable care not just for our own safety, but for the safety of others.

This is amplified when training and/or diving with new and inexperienced divers. They will be relying on our knowledge and practical experience to keep them safe. Professional trainers have the additional responsibility of complying with governmental regulations (depending on the country).

Throughout this book and your training you have been shown the facts and how to avoid problems. The gas planning sections of this book play a special role in risk reduction. However, determining the level of acceptable risk needs a new mind-set, a systematic approach to evaluation.

Clearly, the avoidance of DCI is of paramount importance, but there are times when extra care needs to be taken, eg when diving in remote locations like Papua New Guinea where the nearest hyperbaric chamber is in Townsville Australia or in Bikini Atoll that requires a flight to Kwajalein Atoll. In both cases a special flight will need to be arranged to collect and transport you to the chamber. This will cost a great deal of money, so be appropriately insured, and it will take a fair amount of time. By the way, the Kwajalein chamber belongs to the military and you may have to wait.

This chapter provides the basis of that systematic approach. However, it is your attitude to risk that is the most important factor.

What is risk assessment?

Risk assessment is simply examining any situation very carefully to see what, if anything, could cause harm to you or others. The purpose of risk assessment is to avoid people getting hurt or becoming ill. Accidents and illness can ruin lives.

Risk assessment is a tool that allows you to examine your diving and dive sites, to avoid or reduce risk of harm to a minimum.

The fun should outweigh the risk.

You will need to identify hazards and decide which are significant. The Health and Safety Executive say that the best approach is to remove the hazard if at all possible. However, they do recognise that this is sometimes impossible. For example, if you are going diving it is impossible to avoid decompression. So, where complete avoidance is impossible, the risk must be reduced to a low level, and then measures put in place to control the remaining risk.

How to assess the risk

Five basic steps have been identified:

- Step 1 - look for the hazards.
- Step 2 - determine those at risk and how.
- Step 3 - evaluate the risks and decide whether the current precautions are appropriate or need adjustment.
- Step 4 - record your findings.
- Step 5 - review your assessment and alter if necessary.

Risk Assessment form/ aide-memoire

g 10.1

Site:	Slack water time:	Date
Step 1 Identify potential hazards		
1a. Shore eg access, wave action, current etc.		
1b. Dock/boarding eg Slipping, height up/down to boat.		
1c. Sea journey eg sea state, slip/falls, dry on zipped up or off.		
1d. On-site eg Tide, shipping, depth, decompression surface cover etc.		
1e. Other – define.		
2. Personnel		
2a. Divers eg experience, sufficient for task, DCI, fast ascents etc.		
2b. Trainees eg Basic trainee, buoyancy control, ascents, gas consumption. Advanced trainees etc.		
2c. Boat crew eg Slips/falls ie tidy deck, gear stowed etc.		
2d Public eg slips, trips and falls on equipment etc. Falling dive cylinders etc Exposed boat prop.		
3 Appropriate precautions.	**4. Action taken**	
Step number		
5. Update	**Step 6. Action taken**	
Step number		

© Bob Cole

The watchwords here are simplicity and practicability, avoid over-complication.

The HSE define the word **Hazard** as "anything that can cause harm" and **Risk** as "the chance, high or low, that somebody will be harmed by the hazard".

It would be wise to prepare a standard Risk Assessment Form for your type of diving as a sample, see Fig 10.1 and appendix 2 This should be used as an aide-mémoire to check each dive and dive site and amend as required.

Step 1 - Looking for the hazards

Walk the site! This means checking the beach, jetty or boat for hazards, eg slippery surfaces, poorly stowed equipment etc. Ask your divers for their views, they may have seen something that you've missed. Get them involved and on your side!

Step 2 - Determine those at risk and how

Relate the risk to people. Think who might be harmed?

A falling cylinder has no conscience: it could just as easily fall on a member of the public as on you or another diver.

On an untidy boat you are more likely to break a leg than suffer DCI.

Step 3 - Are the current precautions appropriate?

You may have evaluated the dive and the site on a previous occasion. However, you need to be sure that the situation has not significantly changed since the last time and that your precautions remain valid.

Ask yourself: can I get rid of the hazard? For example, a stationary but unguarded boat propeller, on a crowded beach, is a potential danger to a falling child. To reduce exposure to the hazard, the propeller could be either fenced off or covered up.

Step 4 - Record your findings

In the event of an accident, you may be called upon to show that you did take suitable and sufficient precautions.

You may need to show that:

- a proper check was made
- you asked who might be affected
- you dealt with all obvious significant factors
- the precautions were reasonable and the remaining risk was low

Keeping a written record will help reduce wasted time on the next dive and help you to quickly identify any changes that have taken place.

These records could be invaluable if you become involved in an action for civil liability.

Step 5 - review your assessment and alter if necessary

Life is dynamic and therefore, you need to keep an eye on new equipment and techniques which could lead to new hazards.

If there is any significant change, adjust your assessment to protect against the new hazard. Avoid trivial changes.

Learn from others

Learn by the mistakes of others. You will not live long enough to make them all yourself!

Chapter 11
DCI recognition, first aid and treatment

Introduction

The risk of decompression illness (DCI) after and even during ascent is intrinsic and cannot be avoided. Given that this is a fact of life it is wise to train and plan to deal with it.

There is no doubt that a stricken diver's best chance of surviving a DCI hit without residual problems (eg brain damage, paralysis, sexual dysfunction, death etc) is prompt treatment. This makes it imperative that the dive team is trained to deal with this and other types of emergencies and has the appropriate level of equipment.

The magic bullet

Decompression illness is caused by inert free-gas within the blood and tissues disrupting the body's normal functions. The trick is to encourage this gas to diffuse out of the bubbles and to dissolve into the blood so that it can exit the body in the normal way. In the first instance, first aid must be given to the stricken diver. The magic bullet or wonder gas that does the trick is pure oxygen, which is given to the casualty to breathe.

Since the breathing gas now contains no nitrogen the pressure gradient increases, forcing the free-gas to exit the bubbles and into the blood so it can leave the body via the lungs. Sounds simple. Well it is, but it is not the complete story. To achieve a satisfactory outcome, all suspected DCI casualties must be taken to a recompression facility to receive professional medical treatment from a qualified hyperbaric doctor.

Decompression illness is a multi-faceted problem that has a considerable number of manifestations. The following is a list of common symptoms and signs, but it is not exhaustive:

Symptoms *(what the diver tells you)*

Pain in limbs joint or joints	Dizziness
Skin itching	Numbness

Unusual or extreme fatigue	Pins and needles
Mental confusion	Loss of sensation
Visual disturbance (tunnel vision)	Paralysis or weakness
Chest pains	Shortness of breath
Staggering	Nausea
Collapse	Unconsciousness
Loss of bladder or bowel functions	

Signs (what you can see)

Blotchy red or blue skin rash	Staggering
Choking	Loss of sensation
Loss of strength	paralysis
Collapse	Unconsciousness

For an on-site DCI check list see appendix 3

In some situations, symptoms and signs can merge because it comes down to who recognises them first or they may be seen by both parties; casualty and first aider. In truth, it really doesn't matter where the recognition comes from as long as it comes.

Diver denial

A major problem to prompt first aid and evacuation is "diver denial". Denial is not a diving thing, it's a survival thing and may also be an embarrassment thing. A survival thing, because it's no good stopping to deal with a minor injury when being chased by a dinosaur - it goes that far back. An embarrassment thing because no one likes to look a fool.

DCI is not a foolish thing. It's a sports injury and we need to deal with it as such - there should be no stigma.

Looking at the above inexhaustive list of symptoms and signs creates the question - when do I treat a suspected DCI casualty? The answer is far simpler than you might think . . . Simply treat all strange or unusual feelings that appear after a dive as DCI, until proven otherwise. In other words get'em on to oxygen and call the coastguard for help/advice.

Types of DCI

Decompression illness (DCI) has two main branches: Decompression sickness (DCS) and arterial gas embolism (AGE). Taking AGE first, this is not generally related to excess bottom time. Its cause is related to either a burst lung (pulmonary barotrauma), a hole in the heart (PFO) or very fast ascents. In this type of DCI the onset of symptoms is usually very fast, within the first half hour after surfacing or sooner, and even during the ascent. Of the two major types this is by far the worst condition, usually involving the central nervous system (CNS), it may even be life threatening.

On the other hand DCS is associated with dive time and depth ie gas loading and is often caused by poor control of bottom times/depth and ascents.

The DCI response

In any situation where there is any suspicion of DCI the basic response should be automatic:

- Recognition.

- Administration - oxygen and fluids.

- Emergency evacuation.

- Recompression.

Prompt appropriate first aid action followed by equally prompt hyperbaric treatment offers the best chance of avoiding residual problems.

Early recognition is the key to a satisfactory resolution of the symptoms and damage repair.

The removal of nitrogen and any other inert gas from the breathing gas is achieved by breathing pure oxygen. The O_2 window is now wide open. In some instances the symptoms may get worse before they start to improve. This is a normal reaction. In addition to the administration of oxygen it is very important that the casualty drinks plenty of water - at least one litre in the first two hours.

Whilst this first aid is being applied the Diving Officer or Dive Master must contact the coastguard for assistance. The coastguards will act as the incident managers arranging for the medical team and air transport from the boat to the recompression facility.

When the helicopter arrives at the boat, follow the instructions given to you by the crew - a great deal of static electricity is generated by the helicopter, so do not touch the descending crew member or any lines or ropes until instructed to do so.

The administration of oxygen may alleviate DCI symptoms. This is not a reason to think that DCI has gone away. All suspected DCI casualties must be recompressed unless a qualified hyperbaric doctor says there is no need.

Oxygen, be careful!

Oxygen might be a wonder gas or the magic bullet, but there is another side to the equation. Although oxygen itself does not burn it does enable other things to burn. In fact, given the right condition it can cause a spontaneous explosion*.

*The difference between fire and an explosion is the rate at which combustion occurs. As an example submarine blasting gelatine burns at 9 miles per second. That's fast!

Fig 11.1

The Fire Triangle

Heat

Fuel

FIRE

Oxygen

Equipment needs to be oxygen compatible and oxygen clean, ie in so-called "oxygen service" before it can be safely used. Cleanliness and absence of grease, hydrocarbons even the grease from your finger print is essential.

There are three things necessary to cause a fire or explosion: heat, fuel and oxygen - the so-called "Fire Triangle", see Fig 11.1. There is more than enough oxygen in air to help start a fire, but with pure oxygen the chances increase many times. Heat can come from many sources: engines, compressors etc. Given the right conditions any material will burn - even a steel diving cylinder. Proper training is essential.

Preparation

This book is not a substitute for proper training, you are strongly advised to seek formal first aid oxygen administration training from a recognised diver training agency.

DCI is a statistical problem: dive enough and it's bound to

happen. If it's bound to happen, prepare to deal with it and that includes diver denial. It is always worth remembering that it is unwise to assume that a diver with a problem is in any fit state to make a reasoned judgement on DCI. The very character of the disease can disturb reasoning.

Positive pro-active management will help. Since DCI is no respecter of experience or status, it can happen to diving officers and novices alike. In view of this, a DCI accident action plan would help. The following procedure is recommended:

- Determine a "Base health-line" for each diver in the team, ie existing aches and pains, medication and colour of urine, see example form in Fig 11.2. This form tells the Diving Officer of any special issues and divers will be aware that these important questions will be asked, thus acting as an aide memoire about dehydration etc.

- Set up a DCI/accident management team and backup team eg:

  - *Diving Officer (DO) + Backup DO.*
  - *DCI observers (DCI-O) + Backup DCI-O.*
  - O_2 *administrator + Backup O_2 admin.*
  - *CPR team + Backup CPR team*

Clearly DCI can hit the Diving Officer, therefore it is important to appoint a backup DO.

DCI observers are members of the dive team appointed to take the time to monitor the group for signs of potential problems and report to the DO. The aim is to protect divers and it should be open and above board, not a secret service.

Appointed oxygen administrators and a CPR team should be normal practice, so should the appointment of backup teams.

In addition to the management plan there will need to be an

Fig 11.2

Health base-line Form

Diver's name, contact and contact phone number	Brief description of current health. eg aches and pains, headaches, feeling off colour, medication etc	Colour of urine, eg: D = dark yellow M = medium yellow L = light yellow
1. Fred Bloggs -Wife 01234 543661	None	M
2. Mary Smith – June Browne – 0998 087771	Left wrist	L
3. John Jones – Valerie 01122 13456	None	D
4. Mike Binns – Wife Jean 04433 26849	Small of back Anti-inflammatory pills	M
5. Caroline Green - Mother 7496 231921	Headache	L
6. Keith Burton – Wife 01324 64872	Sore throat	M
7.		
8.		
9.		
10.		
11.		
12.		

© Bob Cole

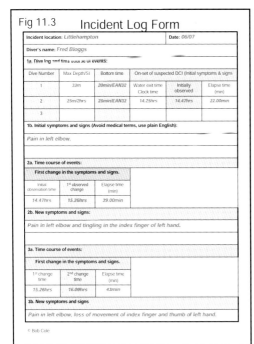

Fig 11.3   Incident Log Form

Incident location: *Littlehampton*   **Date:** *06/07*

Diver's name: *Fred Bloggs*

1a. Dive log and time soul ue of events:

Dive Number	Max Depth/SI	Bottom time	On-set of suspected DCI (Initial symptoms & signs)		
			Water exit time Clock time	Initially observed	Elapse time (min)
1	33m	20min/EAN32			
2	25m/2hrs	25min/EAN32	14.25hrs	14.47hrs	22.00min
3					

1b. Initial symptoms and signs (Avoid medical terms, use plain English):

Pain in left elbow.

2a. Time course of events:

First change in the symptoms and signs.

Initial observation time	1st observed change	Elapse time (min)
14.47hrs	15.26hrs	39.00min

2b. New symptoms and signs:

Pain in left elbow and tingling in the index finger of left hand.

3a. Time course of events:

First change in the symptoms and signs.

1st change time	2nd change time	Elapse time (min)
15.26hrs	16.09hrs	43min

3b. New symptoms and signs

Pain in left elbow, loss of movement of index finger and thumb of left hand.

© Bob Cole

evacuation plan and back-up and first aid oxygen, still drinking fluid and other first aid equipment.

DCI progress

DCI is a dynamic disease that changes with time. This progression, if recorded, may help the hyperbaric doctor in the treatment of the casualty. The **DCI Incident Form** shown, completed, in Fig 11.3 can be used to plot the changes that occur, it should be completed in plain English and accompany the casualty to the hyperbaric chamber.

Medicine (pain killers)

Pain killers can mask symptoms and must not be given to suspected DCI casualties or those who have missed stops or made a fast ascent etc.

Missed stops/fast ascents

Missed decompression stops, even without symptoms, should be treated as a full blown DCI. It is highly likely that the diver will be fizzing like a recently cracked coke can!

Equally, fast ascent must be treated in the same way.

Where a diver, for any reason, makes an inappropriate ascent the following procedure is recommended:

For a diver with no signs or symptoms of DCI. Within a maximum target time of five minutes of surfacing:

- *land the diver.*
- *administer 100% oxygen for a minimum of 60 minutes.*
- *keep the patient still and quiet.*
- *contact the emergency services to obtain hyperbaric medical advice.*
- *have the patient drink one litre of still non-alcoholic and caffeine free fluid during the first hour and another litre during the next 12 hours.*

- *suspend the patient's diving activities and all other strenuous activities for a minimum of 24 hours and stay within easy reach of a phone.*

- *monitor the patient for any abnormal signs or symptoms.*

If any signs or symptoms appear, urgently dispatch the patient to a hyperbaric facility.

In-water recompression

In western countries such as Britain, recompression chambers can be reached in a very short period of time and in-water recompression is unwise and is actively discouraged. Re-immersing a suspected DCI casualty in cold tidal waters may lead to dangerous complications.

In remote locations the problems are very different. Often there is no recompression chamber and an aeroplane may have to be flown to pick-up and transport the injured diver hundreds even thousands of miles to treatment. Under these circumstances special shallow water first aid recompression may be used, see appendix IV.

Recap

For the best resolution of DCI symptoms and the avoidance of residual effects:

- Recognition must be early.

- Administration of oxygen and fluids needs to be prompt.

- Avoid pain killers, they may mask symptoms.

- Evacuation needs to be swift.

- Recompression is a must.

Chapter 12
An Introduction to Practical Decompression
(In the real world)

Introduction

Decompression theory is very useful in identifying the limitations of the current decompression systems and great for flagging up those items of diver behaviour that require additional attention. However, there is a need to discuss some of the practical options regarding implementation. Furthermore, practical training and lots of practise of these skills is essential to ensure safer diving.

Team work

This is a very practical section and the first thing that needs to be appreciated is that safe decompression is a team effort: not just the diving team but also the surface support team. This team may be just the skipper of the dive boat. But unless the skipper is involved with and signs on to the dive and the surfacing procedures being adopted there is no surface support! Clear unambiguous procedures and signals must be adopted and understood by all. This will mean training and testing - Don't forget the skipper.

For straight forward resort diving where safety-stop bottom times will not be exceeded, simple arrangements will suffice. Under these conditions divers should make their plans known to the Diving Officer (Dive Master). These should include maximum depth, bottom time and surface-to-surface time and gas supplies - diving should not commence until agreement with all parties is met, including the skipper.

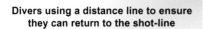
Divers using a distance line to ensure they can return to the shot-line

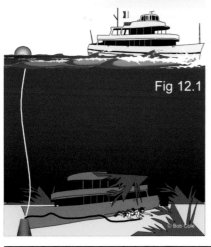
Fig 12.1

Ideally, ascent should be via the shot (or anchor-line or reef/wall), this affords the divers a visual reference point during the ascent and a means of control should buoyancy become a problem. One means of ensuring, as far as is practical, that divers can return to the shot-line is to reel-off using a distance line, see Fig 12.1. At the return point the divers retrace their steps by reeling in the distance-line back to the start.

If diving from a beach, a safe exit point must be identified and a means of return established. Safety-stops can be made at a convenient safe area at an appropriate depth close to the point of exit and must be clearly identified.

Longer decompression hangs

As sport diving becomes more adventurous the need to analyse practical decompression procedures becomes necessary.

There are four main methods open for this type of diving:

- Use the shot-line.
- Shot-line and Free-hang.
- Free-hang.
- Decompression station.

As with club type diving the anchor/shot-line can be used as a decompression reference point.

Divers decompression using jon-lines to stand-off the shot-line

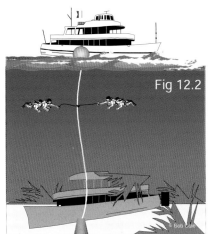

Fig 12.2

When decompression hangs become longer, the tide may impinge on the diver's ability to maintain the desired decompression depth and make life very uncomfortable. Overcrowding on the line may become a problem. With a number of divers on the shot-line at the same time the marker buoy may be pulled underwater compromising safety and stops.

A way to ease this problem is use a jon-line, which is a piece of rope about two metres long, attached to the shot-line to give separation between divers. This eases the downward forces on the marker buoy Fig 12.2. Nevertheless, the inherent problems of using the shot-line are still there.

Shot-line and Free-hang

If the concerns are tide and diver numbers, a part way house is to ascend part way and deploy a delayed-surface-marker-buoy (DSMB) from about 15-12 metres from the surface and drift with the flow, see Fig 12.3. The advantage here is that there is no relative movement

Divers Decompressing on a Free-hang

Fig 12.3

Divers deploying DSMBs from the sea bed and mid-water

Fig 12.4

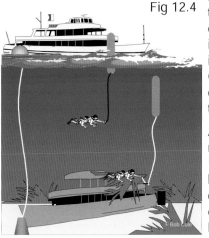

between the divers and the water, so there is relaxed decompression, and all teams drift with the tide in the same direction making recovery by the boat relatively easy. In real life, of course, the teams may drift in somewhat different directions making surface support more difficult.

Free-hanging decompression

In the UK at least, this is a common method of decompressing.

The advantage of this method is that it allows divers to explore a wider area of a wreck or sea bed. The disadvantage is that the reel/line can jam or bird's nest and drag the diver to the surface.

In principle, the method is very simple: at the end of the dive deploy the DSMB from the wreck to the surface. The wreck may be used as a reference point and as an anchor against being pulled to the surface by a jammed reel. Tying the reel off to the wreck with a cord or bungee is the better option. It allows the bag to be filled partially inflated and checked out before it is fully inflated and released to the surface, Fig 12.4. Once the bag has reached the surface the cord/bungee can be released from the wreck to allow the ascent to begin.

Alternatively, the DSMB could be deployed mid-water following a free ascent, see Fig 12.4. In both cases, the reel must be hand-held and not tied to any part of the body or the diver's equipment. Care must be taken to ensure that the ascending line does not become entangled in equipment during the process. One way of avoiding entanglement is for the buddy pair to work as a team: one paying out the line from the reel and the other guiding the line through their hands.

One other option, particularly in mid-water, is to use two

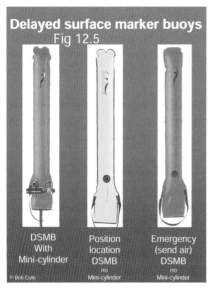

Delayed surface marker buoys
Fig 12.5

| DSMB With Mini-cylinder | Position location DSMB no Mini-cylinder | Emergency (send air) DSMB no Mini-cylinder |

© Bob Cole

reels fixed together. If the primary reel jams swap to the other one.

Reel jams are a real threat. The key here is regular maintenance: reels should be inspected for free running and lines for knots, tangles and fraying. Another potential problem of inflating a DSMB underwater is that the DV may free-flow causing a waste of breathing gas. Options are: use a DSMB with a mini-inflation cylinder (see Fig 12.5), use your exhaust gas or a gas gun connected to the first stage valve of your DV.

Communication with the surface is important. Whilst the first DSMB identifies where the divers are, the divers can call for extra breathing gas/assistance by sending up a second DSMB, see Fig 12.5.

Decompression Stations

For prolonged decompression hangs and to keep a dive team together, in one place, the ideal in-water decompression system is the "decompression station". There are a number of forms.

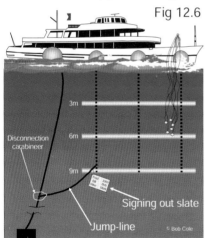

A decompression trapeze with surface supplied EAN$_x$

Fig 12.6

3m

Disconnection carabineer

6m

9m

Signing out slate

Jump-line

© Bob Cole

The idea, as with all good ideas, is very simple indeed. The traditional classic is the "trapeze". A series of bars (tubes) are mounted horizontally, usually on ropes or wires, from a surface support system of large buoys at the various stage-stop depths eg 3, 6, 9 metres etc, see Fig 12.6. Careful attention needs to be paid to the support system; it must be able to support all the divers plus all of their equipment in all expected sea conditions.

This system can be used to support emergency bailout gas as well as decompression gases. In the right sea and wind conditions, the support boat can be tied to the station, and surface demand decompression gas can be supplied to the divers via long hoses and DVs, see Figs 12.6 & 12.7.

Fig 12.7

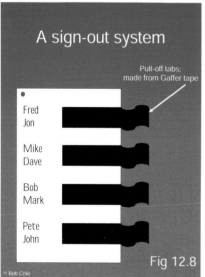

A sign-out system

Pull-off tabs;
made from Gaffer tape

Fred
Jon

Mike
Dave

Bob
Mark

Pete
John

Fig 12.8

An alternative is to use large lorry inner tubes as floats with netting across the bottom to hold surface supplied decompression gas etc. This system is less affected by wind and tide conflicts.

The decompression station is attached to the shot-line via jump-line and a large carabiner that is disconnected to allow the station to drift free after the dive.

On long dives many dive teams use a "sign out" system attached to the jump point. This allows the status of all the divers to be checked before the station is set free.

The "sign out" system can be a slate (white plastic board) on which divers tick off their name with a pencil, or the removal of a clothes peg from a status slate. Another simple method that needs no pencil is a slate with the team names running down one side and a piece of gaffer with a folded tape stuck against each diver's name, see Fig 12.8. On ascent, divers simply peel off the tape adjacent to their name - no pencil or pen required.

The shot-line can be further identified at the dive site by attaching a couple of underwater strobe lights at say three and six metres above the wreck. This should make finding the line easier.

General

If the skipper does not supply the decompression trapeze you will have to make your own. A major consideration is transportability - the tube needs to be of sufficient diameter to allow easy handling underwater, small enough to fit in your car yet long enough to allow the team to use underwater with comfort.

The placing of emergency gas is an important consideration. What to do if a diver is late back to the decompression station? This can be addressed if divers use the two DSMB system. The delayed divers, finding the decompression station has gone, deploy a yellow DSMB indicating their position and if followed by a red DSMB to indicate a problem or the need for extra breathing gas. Notes can be written on a slate and attached to a DSMB telling the surface team the exact situation.

Training and good communications between the whole team, including the boat skipper, is essential.

Chapter 13
Round up

Introduction

The actual cause (aetiology) of decompression illness has not, as yet, been elucidated. This means that there can be no universal first principle system of DCI avoidance. It was with this in mind that this book was written. The advice given will certainly not guarantee complete protection from DCI. It should, however, reduce the risk and there is nothing in here that will cause DCI.

Progression

What I am saying is that the science of decompression is incomplete, but it is steadily progressing and improving.

Traditional dissolved gas models are being up-dated with systems that incorporate free-gas (bubble) components; and for the first time there is a common direction of slow ascents and safety-stops emerging. These are all good moves, and we certainly seem to be moving in a common direction.

Diver education

As in all walks of life, education should not stop the day school finishes. This really is the starting point of a life-long update or "continuous personal development". It is for the diver to maintain a grip on "best practice" and on current developments and this book, I hope, is part of that process.

Summary

To summarise, the decompression algorithms used both in tables and PDCs are designed on the concept that blood flow (perfusion) around the body during diving, decompression and the surface interval is within certain limits, ie not too fast and not too slow. It is for the diver to evaluate the environmental conditions and their expected personal behaviour before, during and after diving as part of the preparation and planning process. The diver should also select decompression equipment equal to the task at hand.

The guinea-pigs used to develop decompression systems were men: naval and commercial divers. Women were not really a part of the process. However, now women are diving in ever greater numbers. The information given in this book, for the reasons mentioned above, is scant. Nevertheless, women seem to dive with no more problems than men. However, it would seem wise for them to follow personal feelings and tolerances. The question of diving while pregnant is still a hot issue, and one that the medical profession errs on the side of caution.

Personal decompression computers (PDCs) are getting evermore able to process information and to offer advice, not just on decompression but on gas consumption etc. Remember the first paragraph of this chapter!

Computers are being relied upon in all walks of life from the money markets to rocket science. Diving adds the dimension of personal death or disability, be sure you have an escape route. A PDC is a "tool" that needs to be used with skill [PDCs give a false impression of ease and safety]. In fact PDC diving is advanced diving, it takes the diver nearer to the conventional edge/limit of so-called safe table diving.

With PDC diving the need to account for environmental conditions and behavioural factors increases as does the need for a back-up plan ie escape route.

A better understanding of physiology and physics can only help the diver understand and implement the DCI avoidance strategies.

The three main areas of concern are:
- excess workload
- skin cooling, and
- micro-bubble generation

Clearly, PDCs are becoming more adept at assisting the diver. However, PDCs do not make decisions. That is the diver's job. Recognition and acknowledgement of a problem or potential problem is the first step in disaster avoidance.

It is always good to have a number of strategies to help avoid DCI, eg hydration control, behaviour review, DeeP stops, slow ascent and safety-stops, etc etc. But it is very important to develop a strategy package as part of your dive planning system.

The out-of-gas situation is a growing problem. It is a situation that is guaranteed to make a bad situation worse once beyond the glass ceiling of the decompression stop.

Gas calculations need not be tedious or hard. At the very least the tables in this book offer a simple straightforward solution, but if you prefer there are software applications available for the job. Whatever you do, be sure that you have enough gas for the situation, particularly for "deeper-than-tabulated" decompression stops.

Diving, nowadays, has progressed beyond the one size fits all and it is possible for divers to move on to more advanced techniques such as Nitrox, Trimix and Rebreathers. The introduction given in this book must be accompanied by appropriate training given by suitable instructors. Training agencies offer good training packages, but it is always worthwhile taking the time to check out the instructor before you sign-on.

The world is following America in litigation. Mess up and someone will take you to court. Even if that were not the case "risk assessment" is a worthwhile precaution.

It only takes a few minutes to think about avoiding hazards. Take the time to reduce the risk of hurting yourself and others.

Decompression is about teamwork; not just the diving team, everyone including the boat skipper and attendants. Include everyone in your plans and share the information with them. Take the team with you, don't set them against you.

Good luck with your diving.

Appendix 1
Glossary of terms

Aetiology: The science and study of the cause of disease and their mode of operation.

Alveoli: Terminal air-sacs in the lungs where gaseous exhaling takes place.

Ambient: Surrounding. In this book surrounding air or water pressure.

Artery: Major blood vessel which carries blood away from the heart to the body.

Arterial gas embolism: Gas bubbles in the arterial circulation of the body.

Atrium: Upper chambers of the heart; the right receives returning, de-oxygenated, blood from the veins and pumps it to the right ventricle. The left atrium receives oxygenated blood from the lungs and pumps it to the left ventricle.

Aural barotrauma: Damage caused to the ear(s) due to pressure changes during the descent or ascent.

Central Nervous System (CNS): The brain and spinal cord.

Cerebral arterial gas embolism (CAGE): Gas bubbles in the brain supplied by the arterial circulation. This may result in neurological decompression illness and brain damage.

Decompression: Any reduction in ambient pressure. All dives involve decompression.

Decompression illness (DCI): Usually associated with gas coming out of solution in the venous circulation and/or tissues following decompression.

Diffusion: Movement of gas molecules in the body from a region of high concentration to a region of lower concentration; spreading out.

Embolism: Obstruction of a blood vessel by a travelling blood clot or particle of matter. Gas - The presence of gas or air bubbles in a blood vessel, often caused by a pulmonary (lung) barotrauma.

Free-air capacity: The free-air capacity of a cylinder is obtained by multiplying the water capacity (WC), in litres by the working pressure (WP), in bar.

Oedema: An excess amount of fluid in the body tissues.

Pulmonary barotrauma: A burst lung caused by a major or local excess pressure.

Sport Diver: Any diver diving for fun and not for remuneration:

- *Resort Diver* - divers who dive only on holiday, usually under the supervision of a Diver Master.
- *Club Diver* - divers who dive in their on country as well as on holiday.
- *Technical Diver* - divers who plan and manage their own dives beyond the safety-stop limit either on Air, Nitrox, Mixed Gas or using a Rebreather.

Stops: A predetermined wait for a specified time at a designated depth following a dive and prior to surfacing, during which time excess nitrogen is gassed-off:

Safety stop - A cautionary stop following any no-stop dive.

Stage stop - A mandatory decompression stop required when the diver has exceeded the no-stop bottom time.

Surface interval: The interval, on the surface, between dives during which time excess nitrogen is off-gassed - a Zero Metre Decompression Stop.

Valsalva's manoeuvre: Ear clearing achieved by pinching the nose and gently blowing.

Vein: A major blood vessel returning blood to the heart.

Water capacity (WC): A method of measuring the gas capacity of a diving cylinder (tank). The cylinder is filled with fresh water: the volume of water, in litres, is the water capacity (WC) of the cylinder. The free air, available to the diver to breathe, is obtained by multiplying the WC (in litres) by the cylinder pressure (in bar), eg a cylinder with a WC 12 litres, charged to say 232 bar has a free gas capacity of 2784 litres.

Appendix 2
Useful Pro-formas

Risk Assessment form/aide-memoire

Site:	Slack water time:	Date:

Step 1. Identify potential hazards

1a. Shore
eg: access to & from, wave action, current etc.

1b. Dock/boarding
eg: Slipping, height up/down to boat etc.

1c. Sea journey
eg: sea state, slips/falls, dry suit on and zipped up or off etc.

1d. On-site
eg: tide, shipping, depth decompression limit, surface cover etc.

1e. Other
define

2. Personnel

2a. Divers
eg: experience, sufficient for task, DCI, fast ascents etc.

2b. Trainees
eg: Basic trainee, buoyancy control, ascents, gas consumption. Advanced trainees etc.

2c. Boat crew:
eg: slip/falls ie tide deck, gear stowed etc.

2d. Public:
eg: slips, trips and falls on equipment etc. Falling cylinders etc. Exposed boat props.

3. Appropriate precautions	Step 4. Action taken.
Step number	

5. Update.	Step 6. Action taken.
Step Number	

* Delete as necessary – Bob Cole ©

Diving Officer's Pre-dive Check List

Reference number: /20 · ·
Diving Officer:
Approval given Yes/No* signed ....   Date: · · / · · /20 · ·

Check list	Outcome
1. Dive Site, boat and skipper:	
2. Has the DO given permission for this dive?	*Yes/No

3. Timings:
     I.   Assembly time:
 	
     II.   Slack-water time:
	
	I.
	
	 II.

4. Purpose of dive? eg Fun, training, experience ie F, T, E	
5. Are all attendees fit to dive?	
6. Number of divers and instructor/trainee ratio, eg 12:9.3 (ie 12divers; 9 divers/3 trainees)	

7. Depth limit of trainee divers, eg
    I.   Michael Smith 18m
    II.   Sheila Brown 30m
    III.   etc
    IV.   etc
    V.   etc
	
	I.
	II.
	III.
	IV.
	V.

8. Who will take the oxygen, water and first aid kit?
     I.   Named person:
 	
     II.   Are the O_2 cylinders, water containers and 1st aid kit full?
	I.
	
	 II. *Yes/No

9. Means of communication: ships radio (SR)/Mobile phone (MP) or both	* SR/MP/both

10. Weather report:
     I.   Wind direction
     II.   Wind force
     III.   Sea state
     IV.   Surface viz
     V.   etc
	
	I.
	II.
	III.
	IV.
	V.

11.
     I.   Coastguard telephone number
 	
     II.   Date & time coastguard informed of departure, dive site & boat name.
	
	I.
	
	 II.

12. Documentation: Risk Assessment (see overleaf), Dive plan, Health Base-line, DCI incident form.	*Yes/No
13. Name of Back-up DO.	
14. Names of appointed DCI observers.	
15. Names of Oxygen team and Oxygen Back-up team.	
16. Names of CPR team and Back-up CPR team.	

*Delete as necessary - Bob Cole ©

Health base-line

Diver's name, contact and contact phone number	Brief description of current health. eg aches and pains, headaches, feeling off colour, medication etc	Colour of urine, eg: D = dark yellow M -= medium yellow L = light yellow
1.		
2.		
3.		
4.		
5.		
6		
7		
8.		
9.		
10.		
11.		
12.		

© Bob Cole

Suspected DCI Incident Log

Incident location:				Date	

Diver's name.

1a. Dive log and time course of events:

Dive number	Maximum depth	Bottom time	On-set of suspected DCI (initial symptoms and signs)		
1			Water exit time Clock time	Initial observation: Clock time	Elapse time: (mins)
2					
3					

1b. Initial symptoms and signs (Avoid medical terms, use plain English):

2a. Time course of events:

First change in the symptoms and signs.		
Initial observation: Clock time	1st observed change: Clock time	Elapse time: (mins)

2b. New symptoms and signs:

3a. Time course of events:

Second change in the symptoms and signs.		
1st observed change Clock time	2nd observed change: Clock time	Elapse time: (mins)

3b. New symptoms and signs:

© Bob Cole - 1990

Appendix 3
On-site check list for Decompression Illnesses

Introduction

This check list provides a sound basis for non-medical people who have had some formal training to check for DCI. However, it is not as thorough or exhaustive as an examination done by a diving doctor. It is intended for use in the more remote locations of the world where medical help will take a long time to reach. You should not waste time using it in the UK, Europe, USA etc where help is at the end of a telephone and a relatively short journey away.

It is strongly recommended that you seek further training in the recognition of decompression related illnesses.

Early recognition and prompt treatment of these conditions is the diver's best and only chance of complete recovery.

If there is any doubt as to the cause of a diver feeling unwell, treat as decompression related and call for expert medical help.

Many cases, however, leave no doubt as to the cause. But there is an increasing number which have such subtle symptoms as to be disregarded by the diver and/or Diving Officer. These are possibly the "type II" Decompression Illnesses, of the neurological kind, which may develop into CAGE, PARALYSIS, SENSORY DEPRIVATION etc.

Neurological check list

The outcome of these tests should be noted on paper.

Mental status

Does the diver know: a. who he/she is? b. where he/she is? c. what time it is?

Eyes

Can the diver see?

Instruct the diver to hold his/her head still. Then hold up your hand, about 0.5m in front of his/her face showing say, three fingers. Ask the diver to count the number of fingers shown - use three different numbers of fingers.

Now have the diver follow the movement of your hand with his/her eyes without moving the head. Move your hand up and down, then from side to side. Be sure that both eyes follow your hand in each direction. Look for rapid oscillation of the eye balls, this may indicate brain damage.

Face

Ask the diver to smile. Check that the smile is equal on both sides of the face. One side failing to conform means trouble.

Using the back of your finger, lightly run your hand across one side of the diver's forehead. Confirm this can be felt. Repeat on the other side, confirm the sensation is about the same. Any deviation indicates trouble. Now repeat across the cheeks and chin.

Hearing

Holding your hand close to the diver's ear, rub your forefinger and thumb together; ask the diver to confirm this can be heard. With the diver's eyes shut, move your hand 0.5 to 1.0m away and then repeat. Have the diver indicate when he/she hears it again. Repeat at the other ear.

Shoulders

Ask the diver to shrug his/her shoulders, both sides should move evenly. Check for muscle tone by bearing down, simultaneously, on both shoulders while the diver shrugs.

Gag

Ask the diver to swallow. Watch the "Adam's apple" move up, and then down.

Tongue

Have the diver stick out his/her tongue in the centre of his/her mouth. Deviation to either side indicates a problem.

Muscle strength

Check that the muscle strength appears equal: a. in the arms, b. in the legs

a. Arms. Bring both of the diver's elbows level with the shoulders, hands touching in the centre of the chest. Now ask the diver to resist as you pull his/her arms away from the body then push towards the body. Bear down on the arms, then up.

b. Legs. With the diver in the sitting position, have him/her push out against you then pull back with both legs simultaneously. Now lying the diver down, ask him/her to lift his/her legs against your pressure at the ankles, then lower them while you provide resistance underneath.

Body sensory check

Using the same technique you used on the face run your hand across the shoulders, down the back; chest; abdomen and each arm, upper and lower inside and outside. And now over the buttocks. This should be done one side then the same area on the opposite side of the body to gain comparison before moving to the next part of the body.

Balance and co-ordination

With the diver standing feet together eyes closed and arms outstretched he/she should have no difficulty in maintaining balance (take into account boat movement). Have the diver touch your finger, held 0.5m away, and then his/her nose. As rapidly as possible.

Important

Any part of this examination that does not appear to be normal may indicate serious decompression illness. Discontinue the remainder of the tests and contact a recompression chamber at once.

Information required by the recompression chamber

- What type of dive did the casualty make? eg Depth, duration.
- How many dives were made in last 24 hour period?
- Take dive log books.
- The casualty's dive partner should also attend the recompression chamber at the same time.

Appendix 4
DCI symptoms and signs

Symptoms (what the casualty tells you)

This not an exhaustive list.

Pain in a limb joint or joints.

Skin itch.

Unusual or extreme fatigue.

Mental confusion.

Dizziness.

Numbness or pins and needles.

Visual disturbance (eg tunnel vision).

Paralysis or weakness - local or general.

Loss of sensation.

Inability to control bowel or bladder functions.

Chest pains, shortness of breath.

Staggering, nausea.

Collapse or unconsciousness.

Signs (what you can see)

This not an exhaustive list.

A blotchy red or blue rash on the skin.

Loss of sensation (numbness).

Loss of strength in movement - paralysis.

Staggering.

Choking, shortness of breath.

Collapse - unconsciousness.

IMPORTANT:

Treat any unusual symptom or sign as DCI until proven otherwise. Check with a hyperbaric doctor.

First Aid treatment

- Contact the emergency services.

- Place the casualty in a position of maximum comfort/safety. If unconscious place on left hand side, head down in the recovery position.

- Do not administer any pain killing drugs.

- Administer 100% and give still fluid (water) - transport to a hyperbaric facility.

- Monitor pulse and breathing.